CONSCIENCE AND GUILT

Appleton Psychiatry Series

edited by

THOMAS F. DWYER, M.D.
FRED H. FRANKEL, M.D.
MICHAEL T. McGUIRE, M.D.

Department of Psychiatry
Massachusetts General Hospital
Boston, Mass.

APPLETON-CENTURY-CROFTS
Division of Meredith Corporation
New York

CONSCIENCE AND GUILT

JAMES A. KNIGHT, M.D.

Professor of Psychiatry
and Associate Dean
Tulane University School of Medicine
New Orleans, Louisiana

To
Steven
My Son

Preface

During this century we have added substantially to our understanding of the function of certain emotions in mediating between man's impulsive life and the requirements of civilization. Optimally, a person is guided in directions sanctioned by society, yet simultaneously he establishes a sense of his own unique being. The opportunity is available for personal satisfactions, as well as for acting upon the very society which is shaping him. The young person often hovers between the choice of a long and tedious quest for achievement and the plunge into immediate acts of adventure and diversion.

The complexities of our present world readily separate youth from the values and heroes that seem to give order and meaning to life. One sees in college students a growing alienation from themselves and from one another. Also, while many feel an alienation from the goals of their parents, others wonder if the college experience is relevant in their struggle to define their own goals. Such students find little to affirm and often join the growing ranks of rebels without a cause, filled with protestation but empty of affirmation.

Another complex dimension of our society is the obvious violence on every hand, as well as other types of overt and hidden antisocial behavior. Rap Brown's statement that "violence is as American as cherry pie" has led many to a painful examination of themselves and their country. A recent movie *Bonnie and Clyde* is a part of that examination. By revealing the intimate and public experience of two American gangsters in the 1930's, and by showing the American people's reactions to these gangsters, the film focuses on a horrifying and often obscured fact of American life: many Americans react to killing and violence with the spontaneous delight of children watching fireworks.

Clyde Barrow and Bonnie Parker were trapped in a bleak existence; their exit from that barren life was crime. They began a tour of violence through the west and midwest picking up three others as they moved. Proud and ingenuous, the members of the Barrow gang alternately terrorized and delighted a country characterized in equal measure by courage, callousness, and a good nature.

Critics have generally reacted negatively to this film, probably because they were frightened by its rawness. Also, maybe they have tried to shield the American people from a vision of themselves. Violence in America has some of the same qualities portrayed by the movie *Bonnie and Clyde:* insane joy, casual life taking, pockets of would-be innocence, and quixotic callousness.

America has been accused of being the most criminal nation in the world. Although such a judgment may be questioned, we do have our share of assaults, rapes, and murders. The price manipulations of great industrial concerns, the mass violence in many cities, the subway muggings and the thievery of juvenile gangs, all make it apparent, in James Truslow Adams' words, that "lawlessness has been and is one of the most distinctive American traits." At the same time our puritanical streak is strong in that we are forever searching for some means to cure, suppress, or punish wicked tendencies. Our urge to reform is strong and leads us repeatedly to appoint new commissions, study groups, and task forces to find methods of preventing and correcting deviant behavior.

It seems in order to look seriously at internal and external controls related to human behavior, efforts at assessing responsibility, and struggles of the individual to find his way in a world which does not offer maps with destinations clearly defined.

A large segment of our population looks upon applied science as a major source of salvation; this dependence on applied science has led man to the brink of destruction through nuclear warfare. The potential for destruction has grown beyond man's capacity for control, largely because he has operated on the false premise that the control of nature is so essentially good that man's control of himself is only secondary. In the chapter on "The Dark Side of Man" the focus is on the individual's internal battle to master the dark forces that run counter to the most fundamental moral prohibitions.

Both social scientists and psychotherapists are pushing aside the old views of man that see him only as a concentrated bundle of cause and effect relationships. The old concept of mechanistic and materialistic man is giving way to his new image as a creature in search of meaning with spiritual insights and purposive control. Choice and responsibility are current themes in any discussion of the nature of man. Closely related is consciousness or awareness and an understanding of its varying levels in assessing moral responsibility.

The increasing realization of the importance of guilt for the personal and social health of man commends it for serious attention in this book. Guilt is complex and many faceted; it can proceed from a merciless conscience to destroy life as well as from a healthy conscience to guide it. The problems of guilt are invariably related to the nature, development, and significance of conscience as a special guide in man's personal and social behavior. Conscience is the product of a long and slow development that takes into account the inheritance of the individual and his experiences in his family and social group. Not only is the capacity for and content of conscience examined, but also its faults, failures, and modifications.

One cannot discuss conscience and guilt without mentioning youth's quest for a stable morality amid today's confusion of tongues. By both precept and example the adult world radiates conflicting values and moral ambiguities to youth. Youth continues to ask if the adult world cares enough to help him avoid disaster. And the adult world is somewhat confused by youth who demands freedom from all restraint, while he begs for guidelines and moral structure.

This book is addressed to a broad group of readers. Professionals in the social and psychological sciences will find many of their concerns discussed here, but so also will informed laymen. In fact, the magnitude of conflicts both within and without the individual make topics related to the socialization of man a primary interest for all of us.

I have drawn heavily on my clinical psychiatric experience with patients for illustrative material in this book. Also, when one writes on the subject of conscience and guilt, he is indebted to a host of authorities of the past and present, too numerous to mention.

The encouragement and challenge for writing this book came first from Dr. Edgar N. Jackson. I am indebted also to Mrs. Katherine Blaufuss, School of Public Health and Tropical Medicine, Tulane University, for excellent editorial assistance and to Mrs. Lucile Seitzinger and Mrs. Carroll Wilson, secretaries in Admissions at Tulane Medical School, for their help. Special thanks are reserved for my wife whose wise counsel and editorial skill helped immeasurably at many difficult points.

JAMES A. KNIGHT, M.D.

New Orleans
September, 1968

Contents

CONSCIENCE AND GUILT

1

Anatomy of Conscience

A priest called one day, in an exasperated state, to refer for psychotherapy a 17-year-old boy who that morning had attended mass, taken Holy Communion, and, on walking out of the church, stolen a car parked in the church parking lot.

In rapid sequence the priest asked a number of questions: Does this boy have a defect in his conscience? Could he be what is called a sociopath? Is he emotionally sick? What can we do to help him develop some inner social controls? What are his chances of giving up his antisocial behavior? Could this boy's behavior be a reflection of the problems of adolescence?

The questions asked by the priest are highly relevant and always enter any discussion of antisocial behavior. Unfortunately, these questions are not easy to answer. They do, however, lead us into a discussion of one of the most fascinating topics of human behavior—the conscience.

One of man's most distinctive and impressive characteristics is his conscience. He seems to possess a natural aptitude for socialization and moral responsibility. This faculty in man led Kant to exclaim that nothing was more awe-inspiring than the starry heavens above and the moral law within.

Although the term conscience may not have been used, some word suggesting conscience has appeared in the writings of man since the beginning of recorded history. The Babylonians identified conscience with the heart, and their penitential hymns and psalms revealed their deep sense of guilt and sin.

The Egyptians had a definite sense of right and wrong, and *The Egyptian Book of the Dead* gives a vivid record of man's consciousness of his moral obligations and his potentiality for failure. This book is probably the oldest written record known to us; it antedates the Mosaic Law by many centuries. One passage concerns the confession a dying man was obliged to make in the presence of the Two and Forty Assessors of the Dead. Although the confession is primarily a statement denying evil acts, it reveals a deep moral consciousness. Essentially every commandment of the Decalogue is presaged in this confession, along with a clear understanding of the proper application of these moral principles to everyday life.

The early Greeks and Romans had no special word for conscience but personified its meaning in the form of fierce and tormenting demons which the Greeks called the Erinyes, and the Romans, the Furies. These deities were conceived as terrible beings, relentless in their pursuit of those who had committed murder or other serious crimes. (An example is Oedipus' concern in Sophocles' *Oedipus Rex*.) They were concerned to punish the wicked both in this world and after death—those who had been disobedient to parents, disrespectful toward the aged, and guilty of perjury, murder, and so on. Such an externally projected conscience was a major determinant of the life and social institutions of the people of Greek and Roman antiquity.[6]

The word conscience does not appear in the Old Testament, but a similar meaning is expressed by the general term *heart*. Anyone who reads the Old Testament writers is fully cognizant of the vivid awareness of all aspects of conscience on the part of these writers and the people of whom they write. Later Greek writers, especially the Stoics, employed the term conscience (*syneidesis*). Hence it found its way into the stream of Greek thought and language, and then into the New Testament where it apears about thirty times.*

The basic Greek word *syneidenai* (knowing with oneself or being witness of oneself) was common in popular language. It was used to describe the act of observing oneself, often as judging oneself. In philosophical terminology it received the meaning of "self-consciousness." Philo of Alexandria stressed the ethical self-observation in *syneidesis* and attributed to it the function of *elenchos* (accusation and conviction). The Latin language followed the popular Greek usage and united the theoretical and practical emphasis in the word *conscientia*.

The major questions asked about conscience are: What is it? What is its source? Is it innate in man and does it unfold spontaneously after birth? Is man born only with the capacity for the development of conscience, and does a process of socialization take place primarily during childhood? Is it a transcultural phenomenon?

THE FUNCTION OF INNER CONTROL

Conscience is recognized by most authorities as representing inner controls. With this faculty man is usually able to recognize right from wrong, to act upon the right, and to restrain himself from doing that which he recognizes as wrong. This faculty also operates to pass judgment on an individual's own acts and bring about atonement and restitution through guilt.

* For an excellent discussion of the biblical concepts of conscience, the Hellenistic origin of the term, and its usage in Latin writers, see W. D. Davies' "Conscience" in *The Interpreter's Dictionary of the Bible*.[5] Also the Hellenistic and biblical environment and usage of the word conscience are dealt with succinctly and carefully documented by C. A. Pierce in *Conscience in the New Testament*.[16]

A distinguished anthropologist, a specialist in the communication of culture, was asked if conscience could be only a process of socialization through the internalization of the values of significant persons in the life of the child. He replied that he felt conscience to be much more than this—to be something innate, unfolding apart from a process of socialization. Although, as he confirmed, his opinion was based on intuitive feeling or "faith," he went on to say that the social scientist could unapologetically arrive by faith at such a decision and accept his feelings until they might be displaced by logical, scientific explanation. His view undoubtedly reflects the current attitude of the social scientist toward the less obvious aspects of human nature: a willingness to abandon the rigid determinism of fitting new concepts into cause and effect relationships.

Many hold the theological point of view that conscience is not the voice of God in man himself, but man's own voice. Conscience is the voice of moral man speaking to himself as a moral being and making moral judgments. This voice was placed by God in man at his creation, and man cannot rid himself of it. God has established this monitor in man, to urge him to do what he knows to be right and to restrain him from doing what he regards as wrong. God created man to be a moral being. Thus, he endowed him with the faculty to be moral.

Scholasticism asked: according to what norms does the conscience judge and how are these norms recognized by it? The answer is given in terms of the word *synderesis*—a perfection of our reason that leads us toward the recognition of the good. Thomas Aquinas taught that the first principles of moral action are known to all men without deliberation, but the behavioral implementation of this knowledge requires a kind of liaison between the principle and any given action. The bond between the principle and the act is the conscience. Another way of saying this is that conscience is the bond between law and responsibility. The internal arbiter is brought under the discriminating differentiation and control of the reason in the act of judging both what man knows and what

4

man does. Aquinas speaks of a two-fold judgment: (a) universal principles which belong to *synderesis* and (b) particular activities, which is the judgment of choice and belongs to free choice, that is, the conscience.[1] Lehmann mentions that the Thomist view of conscience is the classic statement, if not the origin, of the popular notion of the conscience as a built-in human device for spot-checking right from wrong.[12]

Nicolas Berdyaev's voice is loud and clear regarding man's endowed faculty to be moral. "Moral life is intertwined with the social, and man's moral experience has social significance. But the first source of moral life is not social. The moral act is first and foremost a spiritual act, and has a spiritual origin. Conscience is not instilled into man by society, although society does affect conscience. Society is an object of moral valuations and cannot be the source of them. Customs and manners have a social origin and are the result of social sanctions, but they are not moral facts."[3]

At another point in his *The Destiny of Man*, he writes:

Conscience is that aspect of man's inmost nature which comes into contact with God, is receptive to His message and hears His voice. . . . Conscience may be repressed, hidden and perverted, but it is connected with the very essence of man, with the divine image and likeness in him. . . . Conscience is the organ of perception of the religious revelation, of goodness, righteousness and truth in its entirety. It is not a special department or function of human nature, but the wholeness of man's spiritual being, its center or its heart in the ontological and not in the psychological sense of the term. . . . Conscience is the spiritual, supernatural principle in man and it is not of social origin at all. It is rather the perversion and confusion of conscience that is of social origin. Conscience is human nature at the depth at which it has not completely fallen away from God but has preserved its connection with the Divine world. Repentance and remorse are only possible because man has a conscience that is not irreparably damaged. Conscience is the meeting point of freedom and grace. What theology describes as the action of grace upon the human soul is the awakening of its depths, the recollection of the Divine

5

source of life. Repentance is the experience of pain and horror at the disharmony between my present life and the memories of the true life for which I was created and from which man fell into this world of sin and sorrow.[3]

A CONCEPT WITH MANY DIMENSIONS

Sigmund Freud viewed the presence of conscience in man as the result of a process of socialization where external parental restrictions and positive values are taken within the person and made a part of his inner life.[9] He would concede that only the capacity for conscience is innate or given, and would insist that the content and application of conscience are developed. Although this traditional psychoanalytic concept of the conscience as delineated by Freud enjoys widespread acceptance in psychiatric and even certain theological circles, many have stressed additional dimensions.

Erich Fromm feels that the concept of conscience can be clarified if one distinguishes between authoritarian and humanistic conscience.[11] He emphasizes that the authoritarian nature of conscience, as Freud describes it, is only a preliminary stage in its development. Humanistic conscience is defined as the voice of our loving care for ourselves, as the expression not only of our true selves, but also of the essence of our moral experience in life. Fromm summarizes his position by stating that the humanistic conscience is the expression of man's self-interest, while the authoritarian conscience is concerned with man's obedience, self-sacrifice, duty, and social adjustment.

Close to Fromm's views are those of the psychologist Maslow.* Maslow identifies an element in conscience that is

---

* A question may be asked about Carl Jung's views of conscience. Actually, Fromm's and Maslow's views are close to Jung's. Jung describes conscience as a structural quality inborn in the psyche, directed to the maintenance of the psychic balance and

related to the intrinsic nature of man and which he designates the "intrinsic" conscience.[13] This is based, at the deepest level of awareness, on the perception of one's own nature, of one's own destiny, of one's own capacities, of one's own call in life. This intrinsic conscience insists that one be true to his inner self and that he not deny it out of weakness or for special advantage. When one buries his talents in the ground or refuses to take a stand in the presence of social injustice, he perceives on some level that he has done wrong to himself and often dislikes himself for it.

The truth-revealing and uncovering techniques such as education and psychotherapy lessen hostility, fear, and greed and increase love, courage, creativeness, and altruism. This leads one to the conclusion that the latter are "deeper," more natural and more basic than the former. Thus, what one calls "bad" behavior is lessened or removed by uncovering, while what one calls "good" behavior is strengthened and fostered by uncovering.

Martin Buber states that although the content of conscience is in many ways determined by the commands and prohibitions of the society to which its bearer belongs, it cannot really be understood as the introjection of one authority or another. The list of admonitions and prohibitions under which an individual has grown up and lives determines only the conceptions which prevail in the realm of conscience but not its existence itself. This is so because of man's unique ability to set at a distance not only his own environment but also himself. Therefore, he becomes for himself a detached object about which he can not only reflect, but which he can, from time to time, confirm as well as condemn.

---

aiming at its wholeness. Its voice can be heard imperatively when it brings an individual into conflict with the conventional moral code and confronts him with the choice between his own personal destiny and the collective way of tradition. Any deviation from the demands laid upon one by his individual destiny or self-development can provoke a reaction of conscience. (For a detailed statement of Jung's view, see his *Civilization in Transition*, section on "A Psychological View of Conscience.")

Buber further defines conscience as the tendency and capacity of man radically to distinguish between those of his past and future actions which should be approved or disapproved. The more or less hidden criteria which the conscience employs in its acceptances and rejections only rarely fully coincide with standards received from our community or particular culture. Connected with this is the fact that the guilt feeling can rarely be wholly traced to a transgression against a taboo of a family or of society. Thus Buber contends that the totality of the order that a man knows to be injured or injurable by him transcends to some degree the totality of the parental and social taboos that bind him.[4]

Buber's concept of man's capacity to make an object of himself is shared by Reinhold Niebuhr. Niebuhr stresses the two paradoxical facts about man.[14] First, man is a child of nature, subject to its vicissitudes, compelled by its necessities, and driven by its impulses. Second, man is a spirit who stands outside of nature. Man is created in the image of God and in this rests his transcendence over nature. As Niebuhr understands this, the image refers to man's capacity for self-transcendence, to make an object of himself. This is the root of "conscience." It gives to man a capacity for objectivity about himself, viewing himself as an object, appraising the degree to which this "object" acts as he would want to be acted toward. This ability and this inborn "golden rule" are the source of morality for Niebuhr. The law of man's nature is love, pointed to by man's self-transcendence. The inevitable condition of man is anxiety. If man trusts in God, he knows his anxious state to be God-intended. His anxiety therefore becomes the energy of creativity—infinite possibilities come as challenges, as leaven for humble achievement in service to God and man.

Paul Tillich speaks of conscience as the silent voice of man's own essential nature, judging his actual being.[19] He goes on to say that even a weak or misled conscience is still a conscience, for man's essential nature cannot be lost as long as man is man. His essential nature can be distorted in the process of actualization but it cannot disappear. Tillich

8

succinctly writes: "The very statement that man is estranged from his created nature presupposes an experience of the abyss between what he essentially is and what he existentially is."

Tillich defines the moral imperative as the demand to become actually what one is essentially and therefore potentially:

It is the power of man's being, given to him by nature, which he shall actualize in time and space. His true being shall become his actual being—this is the moral imperative. And since his true being is the being of a person in a community of persons, the moral imperative has this content: to become a person. Every moral act is an act in which an individual self establishes itself as a person. Therefore, a moral act is not an act in obedience to an external law, human or divine. It is the inner law of our true being, of our essential or created nature, which demands that we actualize what follows from it. And an antimoral act is not the transgression of one or several precisely circumscribed commands but an act that contradicts the self-realization of the person as a person and drives toward disintegration. . . . The "Will of God" for us is precisely our essential being with all its potentialities, our created nature declared as "very good" by God, as, in terms of the creation myth, He "saw everything that He made." For us the "Will of God" is manifest in our essential being; and only because of this can we accept the moral imperative as valid. It is not a strange law that demands our obedience, but the "silent voice" of our own nature as man, and as man with an individual character.[19]

Regardless of differences as to the origin of conscience, both behavioral scientists and theologians agree that without its existence, the human race would have bogged down in a hazardous course, and no kind of civilization would have been possible. They further almost universally agree on certain aspects of its unfolding process in the context of the family and society.

In the chapter on "The Anatomy of the Mental Personality" in *New Introductory Lectures on Psychoanalysis*,

Freud gives his fullest statement regarding the formation of the superego or "the origin of the conscience."[9] He quotes the philosopher Kant as having declared that nothing proved to him the greatness of God more convincingly than the starry heavens and the moral conscience within us. Freud writes that where conscience is concerned God has been guilty of an uneven and careless piece of work, for a great many men have only a limited share of it or scarcely enough to be worth mentioning. Freud goes on to say that though conscience is something within us, it was not there from the beginning. He supports his statement by pointing out that small children are notoriously amoral and have no internal inhibitions against their pleasure-seeking impulses. The function which the conscience undertakes later in life is at first assumed by an external power, namely by parental authority. The child is controlled by proofs of affection or threats of punishment which the child interprets as loss of love, and which must also be feared on their own account. It is only later that the secondary situation arises, in which the external restrictions are introjected or internalized, so that the conscience takes the place of the parental function, and observes, guides, and threatens in the same way as the parents acted toward the child when he was growing up. Thus, in the Freudian sense, the conscience may be thought of as the heir of the properly resolved Oedipus Complex.*

* Freud related conscience development to the resolution of the Oedipus complex. The most straightforward account of how this is supposed to go appears in his paper "The Passing of the Oedipus Complex" (1924).[10] The following account is a brief résumé. Boys and girls take their mothers as their first love objects for the reason that love develops out of dependence on a caretaker. As the boy's love for his mother becomes increasingly passionate, his father becomes an increasingly threatening rival. Eventually a threat of castration is made to the boy or imagined to have been made. Chiefly because of this threat but also perhaps because of his anatomical inadequacy, the boy gives up his mother as a love object, represses his desire for her and his hatred for the father, accepts his father as an ego ideal or model and identifies with him.

Freud is not as precise in his discussion of what happens

10

THE EMERGENCE OF CONSCIENCE

It is characteristic of normal human emotional growth and development that the infant at first feels omnipotent, that all of his needs will be gratified automatically. Eventually, this attitude comes into conflict with the needs and prohibitions of his group and family. His first reactions are frustration and rage directed toward the agent of the frustration, mainly his parents. The usual outcome of this struggle is that because the need to be loved, approved of, and supported by his parents is a more powerful motive, he will relinquish this pleasureful but disapproved behavior in return for this loving parental acceptance. The child is weak and helpless. His parents are big and strong. He uses the politician's dictum, "If you can't lick them, join them." He can do this without losing face because they are big and he is little. He joins them and makes their ways and wishes his ways. This is the beginning of incorporation and identification. In this early stage, he is adopting certain patterns of behavior which emanate from persons and standards outside himself. He is behaving to avoid being caught and punished. This has been described as the period of external morality. But through the process of identification he eventually takes these standards unto himself as his own value system, and thus his true conscience is developed. He incorporates within himself moral standards, heroes about which he reads, important figures in his community such

---

to the little girl. Although the girl's first love object is her mother, she does turn during the Oedipal period to the father and competes with the mother for his love and attention. During this period she interprets the mother as a threat and is afraid of injury or castration at her hands. The mother's threat plus the unevenness of the contest lead the little girl to surrender her desire for the father and to identify strongly with the mother.

11

as his teachers and his minister. These incorporated figures are all called *imagos,* and they become a part of his inner self.* From then on, his conscience will be a restraining and punishing force for unacceptable behavior, and to a great extent, this inner force will replace the necessity of being punished by external authority.

At this stage in his development the child also learns that his parents are not all-powerful and all-knowing. This is a disappointment to him, but he finds comfort in the new knowledge which has been given to him about God, who is all-powerful, all-knowing, and all-seeing—and who stands as the judge and moderator of all behavior. He is now equipped with an internal set of controls and also knows of God who watches over him. Such an understanding of man's moral control has been expressed by numerous poets and philosophers who speak of the stars as the watchful eyes of God. They also speak of the small voice within man, the moral law within him, and so on. Thus, they recognize the existence of both inner and outer controls.

Nietzsche, in the *Genealogy of Morals,* wrote: "The bad conscience is an illness, but an illness as pregnancy is an illness."[15] He was speaking of the creative aspects of the sickness he named "bad conscience." Tillich places Nietzsche with Freud in the group of empiricists who have tried to analyze the genesis of moral conscience in such a way that its autonomy is destroyed.[19] Mankind had to be domesticated, and this was done by its conquerors and ruling classes, according to Nietzsche. These ruling groups, to further their own interests, suppressed by severe punishments the natural instincts of aggressiveness, will to power, destruction, cruelty,

* Before the child learns language, there is evidence to suggest that his thinking is predominantly in pictures. All of us return to this form of visual thinking nightly in our dreams. Apparently the child forms images in his mind of those persons toward whom he has his first strong feelings. These images are composites, bringing together the behavior of each of the key emotional figures, and are called *imagos.* Such *imagos* comprise and shape the content of conscience and the individual pattern of attitudes and feelings toward others throughout life.

and revolution. Although they succeeded in suppressing these trends, they did not succeed in eradicating them. Nietzsche states that the aggressive instincts became internalized and transformed into self-destructive tendencies. Thus man has turned against himself in self-punishment and has separated himself from his animal past from which he had derived strength, joy, and creativity. But his instincts remain alive and require permanent acts of suppression, the result of which is the bad conscience—a great thing in man's evolution, an ugly thing if compared with man's real aim. Nietzsche hopes for the appearance some day of the man who is "beyond good and evil" in the moral sense but who is good in the sense that he is in unity with life universal, with life in its creative and destructive power.

A present-day psychiatrist, Sandor Rado, expresses a viewpoint similar to that of Nietzsche. Rado describes conscience as the self-enforcing agency of the moral code.[18] The moral code does not begin to operate as a moral code unless there is an enforcement agency which operates on its own, that is self-enforcement. Rado asks how the human organism creates this function of self-control. Self-control requires a tremendous force. Where does the force come from? Our predatory ancestors lived by their rage. According to the physiologist Walter B. Cannon, rage is an emergency emotion, an essential item in emergency control. Rage helps the organism to mobilize its available resources for a battle of life and death. This was life in the jungle as the animal kingdom knew it. The human being inherits the same rage. This most important instrument for the survival of the animal becomes the great dynamic for socialization. Why? Because we cannot jump at one another's throats! Thus, what must we do? We have to suppress rage. Who does this for us? The parent or the educator. The result is repressed rage. Rage cannot be repressed for any length of time. Thus it is usually discharged at once on the one who provoked it or on someone else, such as a scapegoat. If there is no one on whom to take out the rage, what does one do? At this point he can learn from the child. A child, in helpless rage, turns the rage against himself and hits himself on the head, or bangs his head against a wall. In this way, he discharges his rage. Rado calls the turning of rage on oneself "retroflexed rage." The "retroflexed rage" is the policeman or guard which we call conscience or self-control.

Under the pressure of retroflexed rage, an individual may develop guilty fear from imagined guilt. He is then bound to torture himself unendingly for the benefit of no one. If he is preoccupied with quieting his needlessly troubled conscience, he has very little time for anything else.

With his rage turned against himself, the individual is safe from the danger of destroying others. He does, however, face the danger of destroying himself on the installment plan. The consequences are many of the illnesses seen in every branch of clinical medicine.

The reasonable response to one's wrongdoing is to apologize, pay damages, and be satisfied with learning one's lesson. Conscience need not be dominated by the mechanisms of the stern punishment system. If children are reared using an appreciative reward system, instead of stern punishment, different results are obtained. Parental reward creates in the child the automatic mechanisms of self-reward known as self-respect and moral pride. Such a reward system builds a healthy conscience where the child learns to use his emotional resources for the intelligent pursuit of realistic goals. Also, it will help him to unfold in full whatever capacity he has for creative achievement. Rado emphasizes that there is no substitute for self-reward, for it is the emotional experience that makes man self-reliant. The reward system awakens and fosters the child's desire for attaining constructive and socially acceptable goals. In this way, the stage is set for pleasurable activity and fulfillment, for the child learns to experience moral pride and to enjoy socially justified self-respect. Such an approach also prepares him for treating others with sincere consideration and respect. The reward system steers clear of indiscriminate permissiveness, for such an attitude is not helpful in child-rearing.

Thus, conscience has a negative and a positive side. The

14

negative side is prohibitive: "Thou shalt not." It is fostered in its growth by strict discipline in early childhood, rigid teachings of an ascetic or extreme puritanical trend, combined with stern punishment or the fear of it. The positive side of the conscience is constructive: "Thou shalt." This positive side corresponds to Freud's ego-ideal. The ego-ideal has as its basis the ideal self, the kind of person one should like to be, and the goal of personality toward which one strives. The ego-ideal may demand, however, an ever increasing perfection. This aspect of the conscience was considered by Freud to be an expression of the admiration which the child felt for the perfection which he in his early years ascribed to his parents. Through the ideal self-image he measures how close he comes to attaining his own ideal, or reaching the goals he has set for himself.

In the flexible, healthy conscience the positive side is emphasized, and the negative side plays only a minor role. In the overdeveloped conscience the negative side is strongly emphasized, and the positive side seems almost non-existent.

BEYOND SOCIALIZATION

I believe that there are dimensions of conscience which extend beyond mere socialization. If rules are related exclusively to the workings of coercion, then the existence of the social order is truly a paradox. It seems absurd to assume that the real or genuine person is one stripped of social inhibitions. The character of a man is not revealed better when he acts lawlessly than when he submits himself to discipline. It is part of human nature itself to take measures to control and direct its own tendencies. As a renowned psychiatrist once said, "Since God gave us the capacity to do evil, He also gave us the capacity to do good." It would not make sense to have the freedom and capacity for one without the other.

Men are willing and able to adopt procedures to curb destructive desires in the light of steadier aims which are also theirs. They are capable of creating barriers to their own impulses. The barriers are a part of them as much as the impulses. Institutions also have been created by man to control his nature. They exist both to reinforce and to change human impulses.

Is there a transcultural dimension to conscience? What is the source of awareness of values beyond one's own society? Does a person have some perspective, some standards of significance, against which one can call into question the codes of one's immediate culture? There seems to be this latent readiness to recognize this wider perspective when a proper opportunity presents itself. Huckleberry Finn's conscience persistently nagged him because he did not report the Negro, Jim, a runaway slave, to Miss Watson. According to the only moral code Huck had been taught, Jim was Miss Watson's property. Thus he ought to paddle ashore and report that Jim was almost free. His guilt even increased when he heard Jim talk of buying or stealing his children, who were the property of another owner. Huckleberry Finn had no doubt in his mind that he was doing wrong, but, because of some wider feeling of human decency which he could not name or identify, he could not bring himself to do what his society called right.

The possibility of transcultural values is a highly complex question. Some aspects of this phenomenon can be seen as selective identification with different aspects of one's culture and the individual combining of these aspects into new forms as well as identifications with wider values beyond those of one's immediate culture. Other aspects remain unexplained. The acceptance of the capacity for and existence of values which transcend "our internalization of the values of our family and group" has to be done possibly as an act of faith. The anthropologist quoted previously may have given the best answer when he was asked if conscience was more than socialization. He replied in the affirmative and said that his answer was a matter of faith.

Tillich adds another dimension to conscience by speaking of the transmoral conscience, which may be so designated if it judges not in obedience to a moral law, but according to its participation in a reality that transcends the sphere of moral commands.[19] A transmoral conscience does not deny the moral realm. It is driven beyond the moral realm by the unbearable tensions of the sphere of law. Tillich declares that in both religion and in analytic psychotherapy, the moral conscience is transcendent—in religion by the acceptance of the divine grace that breaks through the realm of law and creates a joyful conscience, and in depth psychology by the acceptance of one's own conflicts when looking at them and suffering under their ugliness without an attempt to suppress them and to hide them from oneself.

FALLEN ANGELS OR RISEN APES

In any such discussion, the question is always asked, "Are we fallen angels or risen apes?" The miracle of man is how magnificently he has risen. Robert Ardrey in his book, *African Genesis,* stresses his view that civilization has come to man through his observance of nature's most ancient law, that commanding order.[2] And that this instinct for order is humanity's most reliable ally and is much broader and more universal than conscience.

I do not feel that man's devotion to order necessarily needs to be excluded from man's inner controls. This ancient concern for order is seen when a farmer replants his fields again after they have been ruined by flood or drought, where men rebuild cities that other men have destroyed, where we seek to heal and make whole that which is diseased or broken.

One is reminded at this point of Erik Erikson's work in adding some interpretive dimensions to Freud's stages of psychosocial development.[7] He mentions the first year of life as the time when the capacity for religious faith is nurtured or damaged through the development of basic trust or mistrust. Around the second year of life when autonomy and independence begin to bud and when the child is toilet trained, Erikson sees the nurturing of the concept of law and order. Then the development of conscience unfolds during the Oedipal period, years 3 to 6—the period characterized by initiative and movement into a widening world and running into a variety of expectations in the group around the child, causing him guilt, shame, and anxiety.

It would be interesting to hear a discussion between Erikson and Ardrey about the primacy of law and order over conscience in man. One can only speculate as to the implications of the earlier operation of law and order in man.

In looking back over such a discussion, the variety of viewpoints are not given to confuse the reader but to show the many interesting facets of the phenomenon of conscience. There is a Jewish legend that the unborn infant knows the whole of the Torah, but his lips are touched by an angel just before birth and he forgets it all. He has to learn the law again after birth. Thus, as the legend implies, there are great moral values inherent in man, but these must emerge in his life experiences. My work and research leads me to believe that moral values do not emerge automatically but evolve in the conflicted interaction of actual life experience.

Thus an important question is to what extent early child training must or must not exploit the child's helplessness and moral sensitivity to the degree that a deep sense of evil and of incapacitating guilt become unavoidable. Possibly our fear is too great that instinctual forces would run wild if they were not dominated by the negative, prohibitive side of conscience. This view could lead to formulating man's optimum morality as negative morality, to be reinforced by rigid institutions. The answer does not lie in attempts to avoid or deny the sense of badness in children or the "shadow side" in every individual's life, for this would only deepen a sense of secret, unmanageable evil. As our great teachers have always insisted, the answer lies in man's capacity to create order which will give his children a disciplined as well as a tolerant conscience, and a world within which to act affirmatively.[8]

Possibly men will always view the conscience differently, for each will interpret it in the light of his orientation about the nature of man. As for my view of man, it is summarized well by an old Hassidic story, from Martin Buber's *Tales of the Hassidim,* of a pupil speaking about his teacher: "Once I was present at a conversation between my teacher and a widow. He spoke to her of her widowhood with the kind words of a comforter, and she took his words as comfort for her soul, and gathered strength from them. But I saw him weep and I myself could not help weeping; and then I realized that he was speaking to the widowed glory of God."[17]

REFERENCES

1. Aquinas, T. De Veritate, Q. 16: Art. 1; Q. 17: Art. 1.
2. Ardrey, R. African Genesis—A Personal Investigation into the Animal Origins and Nature of Man. New York, Atheneum, 1961.
3. Berdyaev, N. The Destiny of Man. New York, Harper & Row Publishers. The Cloister Library, 1960, pp. 59, 167–168.
4. Buber, M. Guilt and guilt feelings. Psychiatry, 20:121, 1957.
5. Davies, W. D. Conscience. In The Interpreters Dictionary of the Bible. New York, Abingdon Press, 1962, Vol. I, pp. 671–676.
6. de Coulanges, F. The Ancient City. (Trans. by Willard Small.) Boston, Lee and Shepard, 1874, p. 23.
7. Erikson, E. Identity and the life cycle. Psychol. Issues, 1:73, 1959.
8. Erikson, E. Young Man Luther. New York, W. W. Norton & Co., 1958, p. 263.
9. Freud, S. New Introductory Lectures on Psychoanalysis. (Trans. by W. J. H. Sprott.) New York, W. W. Norton & Co., 1933.
10. Freud, S. The passing of the oedipus complex. In Collected Papers. (Trans. by Joan Riviere.) London, Hogarth Press, 1953, Vol. II.
11. Fromm, E. Man For Himself. New York, Rinehart & Co., 1947.

12. Lehmann, P. Ethics in a Christian Context. New York, Harper & Row, 1963, p. 333.

13. Maslow, A. H. Toward a Psychology of Being. Princeton, N. J., D. Van Nostrand Co., 1962.

14. Niebuhr, R. The Nature and Destiny of Man. New York, Scribner's, 1941–1943.

15. Nietzsche, F. The Philosophy of Nietzsche. New York, The Modern Library, Random House, 1954, p. 706.

16. Pierce, C. A. Conscience in the New Testament. London, SCM Press, 1955.

17. Quoted by Neumann, E. Mystical man. Spring, 1961, p. 44.

18. Rado, S. Rage, violence and conscience. Compr. Psychiat., 1:327, 1960.

19. Tillich, P. Morality and Beyond. New York, Harper & Row, 1963, pp. 20–24, 77–81.

2

Choice and Responsibility

The Apostle Paul declared: "I do not understand my own actions. For I do not do what I want, but I do the very thing I hate." (Romans 7:15, RSV). He has described succinctly a basic condition of man: a frequent bondage to hidden determinants of human behavior. One cannot read Maugham's *Of Human Bondage* without deep empathy for Philip Carey. One sees the painful influences upon his behavior of both internal and environmental forces which are actually enslaving tyrannies. One rejoices in his final freedom when he is at last able to choose what he really wants, when he finally becomes his own master after his bleak, bitter years of mortal bondage.

Tennessee Williams, in *Orpheus Descending*, has a character say: "We are prisoners inside our own skins." From such a motivating conviction in the human being, there usually springs the urge to free himself from the prison, to reach insistently for what the mind may imply as unattainable. Deep within this conviction is a dramatic and expansive view of man's condition: a sense of futility playing against a sense of struggle. The implication is that much of survival depends upon the discovery not of the imprisoned self alone but of

21

the many selves co-existing or battling within the person. Thus the inner self is richly populated with shadows of dreams and dreams of shadows, furnishing an endless source of character and conflict. In such a drama, *breaking loose* becomes the central motive.

One of the most important presuppositions of modern psychiatry is that most human behavior is determined by forces within the individual of which he is not consciously aware, unless some special means are adopted to render them accessible. The nature of the unconscious mind can be inferred only indirectly and Freud's essay, *The Psychopathology of Everyday Life*, discusses ways of assessing it.[5] Individuals often act in ways which they themselves are unable to explain. Others may give explanations for their behavior they believe are quite correct but which the trained observer may see as not the real motive. Freud's pronouncements about the dynamic unconsicious are very disturbing, for man likes to think that he is completely rational and can always control his behavior.

Although Freud was not the first to discover unconscious determinants of behavior he went further than anybody before him in stressing the observation and analysis of the unconscious and irrational forces which determine much of man's conduct. Freud also showed that these seemingly irrational phenomena followed certain laws and therefore could be understood rationally. He developed techniques for the understanding of the language of dreams, physical symptoms, and many irrationalities in human behavior. He sought to show that these irrationalities as well as the whole personality structure of an individual were, to a great extent, reactions to the influences exercised by the outside world and particularly by those occurring in early childhood.

BONDAGE OR CHOICE

A problem which still haunts us today, although many feel it is a dead issue, is that of free will and determinism.

CHOICE AND RESPONSIBILITY

One cannot take a close look at contemporary man and his problems without considering this issue. Experimental psychologists are less bothered by the problem than are psychotherapists, although they do not always find it easy to follow the deterministic path. The experimentalist is quick to say that determinism is a necessary assumption for the scientific enterprise.

It is generally conceded that psychoanalysis as a theoretical system is a firm believer in determinism. Karen Horney writes, "I regard as the most fundamental and most significant of Freud's findings his doctrines that psychic processes are strictly determined, that actions and feelings may be determined by unconscious motivations and that the motivations driving us are emotional forces."[9]

Charles Brenner's *An Elementary Textbook of Psychoanalysis* gives a clear statement of the psychoanalytic doctrine of psychic determinism: "The sense of this principle is that in the mind, as in physical nature about us, nothing happens by chance, or in a random way. Each psychic event is determined by the ones that precede it. Events in our mental lives that may seem to be random and unrelated to what went on before are only apparently so. In fact, mental phenomena are no more capable of such a lack of causal connection with what preceded them than are physical ones. Discontinuity in this sense does not exist in mental life."[2] A common misunderstanding expressed in most psychoanalytic writings is that determinism is a basic tenet of the philosophy of modern science and is part of the *Weltanschaung* of all who believe in the value of science.[8] Robert Knight expresses this position clearly when he writes: "Determinism is a fundamental tenet of all science. Dynamic psychology . . . as a science must be deterministic."[12] Knight further states that, "Whatever human actions or decisions seem to indicate the operation of a free will, or a freedom of choice, can be shown, on closer inspection and analysis, to be based on unconscious determinism."[12]

The legal system assumes a middle position on determinism and individual freedom. The criminal behavior of the juvenile or of the psychotic is considered to be determined by circumstance, while the sane adult is construed as being responsible for his behavior. In fact, the legal profession has moved beyond the old rule of determining whether a person can distinguish between right and wrong to a system of limited or partial responsibility. Today, an even newer concept is being considered: Does this individual have the ability to conform his actions to the requirements of the law? If it is decided that he can, then it is assumed that he exercised freedom in committing certain acts. If he were unable to adjust himself to the demands of the law, then he cannot be held responsible for his acts, for he had no freedom of choice because of his illness.

The determinism-indeterminism issue has intrigued man for centuries, and he has discussed his opinions in vast quantities of writings.

The individual who adopts a deterministic position holds that if all the antecedent and concomitant conditions related to a given event, including human events, were fully simultaneously known, it would then be seen that this particular event and no other event could occur. If the same combination of conditions occurred again and were known by this individual, then he could predict this event. Such a hypothesis is untestable; for how could one know when he had all the information, and how could one ascertain and measure simultaneously all the relevant variables? The intrusion of the experimenter, the very process of measurement would modify the events from what they otherwise would have been. Even when these limitations are recognized as existing now, the determinist may still believe that sometime in the future it will be possible to demonstrate the existence of rigid causality throughout the natural order. The indeterminist defends the position that every human being knows by direct experience that he participates in the selection of his own experience, directs his own behavior, foresees its effects, and experiences a sense of responsibility. He contends that this evidence of a basic human freedom is incontestable. He could also point out that the concept of guilt found in all cultures and legal systems—as well as existential guilt which all individuals experience—is evidence for the fact of personal choice with its accompanying sense of personal freedom and responsibility.

Einstein speaks for determinism with these words: "In human freedom in the philosophical sense I am definitely a disbeliever. Everybody acts not only under external compulsion but also in accordance with inner necessity."[3]

A great paradox exists within psychoanalytic writings. In the face of extensive writings about the absolute character of the tenet of determinism, most of these same writings emphasize that the result of psychoanalytic therapy is freedom. Kubie, in an article entitled "Freud's Legacy to Human Freedom," discusses freedom from the neurotic process (which process he defines as control of behavior by unconscious forces) as the Fifth Freedom and the greatest of all freedoms—the freedom to change.[13] Zilboorg states that Freud, from the very outset and always, considered mental health and individual freedom as well-nigh identical.[21] Robert Knight is more restrained than others in his claims for freedom through psychotherapy. What is promised the analytic patient is only the feeling of freedom. Knight states: "This kind of freedom is experienced only by emotionally mature, well-integrated persons; it is the goal sought for one's patients in psychotherapy . . . it . . . is a subjective experience which is itself causally determined."[12]

One should never forget that in spite of Freud's deterministic viewpoint and his great emphasis on the past as the conditioner of the future he involved himself in the treatment of patients with the intention of liberating them, at least in part, from the bondage of the past. Thus, no matter what might have been his theories, in practice he gave vivid testimony for the existence of freedom in man through his capacity to change. If one fails to recognize this, he could surely not in good faith participate in psychotherapy either as therapist or as patient.

The psychoanalytic paradox of believing in psychic determinism and at the same time in attaining freedom over one's life through psychoanalysis has an interesting historical parallel. In the Semi-Pelagian controversy at the Council of Orange, in 529, the Church effected an interesting compromise to which most Christian churches have adhered through the centuries. The Council declared predestination a heresy but asserted that man's innate freedom of will had been so restricted as a result of Adam's Fall that it needs the direct intervention of God to enable it to function in the desired direction. Typical statements from the Council are: "That by the sin of the first man, free will was so turned aside and weakened that afterward no one is able to love God as he ought, or believe in God, or do anything for God, which is good, except the grace of divine mercy comes first to him. . . . We also believe this to be according to the Catholic Faith, that grace having been received in baptism, all who have been baptized, can and ought, by the aid and support of Christ, to perform those things which belong to the salvation of the soul, if they labor faithfully. But not only do we not believe that some have been predestined by the divine power, but also, if there are any who wish to believe so evil a thing, we say to them, with all detestation, anathema."[1]

Probably the most distinctive feature of C. G. Jung's view of man is that it combines teleology with causality and at this point differs strongly from Freud's theory of personality.[11] Man's behavior is conditioned not just by his individual and ancestral history or past (causality) but also by his aims, his aspirations, and where he is going (teleology). Thus the past as actuality and the future as potentiality guide one's present behavior. Jung's emphasis upon the role of destiny or purpose in human development sets him clearly apart from Freud. Jung, moreover, emphasizes that the psychotherapist in his quest for understanding has to be Janus-faced. He looks with one face into man's past and with the other he looks into man's future; and the two views when combined yield a complete picture of man. Jung points out that solely a causal attitude is likely to produce resignation and despair in the individual, since from the standpoint of causality he is a prisoner of his past and cannot undo what has already been done. On the other hand, the teleological or finalistic attitude gives man a feeling of hope and something to live for.

There should be some way to look at this issue of determinism and indeterminism in a way which would be acceptable to the groups who view the issue in an opposing manner. Possibly freedom can be defined as a human capacity for choosing among possibilities of achievement combined with the capacity for action related to the choosing. Such an interpretation of freedom really does not conflict with theories of determinism which stress the role of the past in human behavior. From the standpoint of human behavior, determinism usually looks backward for retrospective analysis, whereas freedom looks ahead for a prospective evaluation of human achievement. It is interesting that Aquinas and Dewey have both suggested that freedom is related to self-determinism. This interpretation of freedom does not imply some kind of miracle which is subject to no law, for freedom has its limitations and its order. Much of the difficulty in resolving the determinism-indeterminism issue is related to a tendency to think of events as necessarily happening to something or to someone, and a tendency to separate past, present, and future in our conceptualizing. Any psychological moment contains within itself the past, the present, and the future. No particular moment can be frozen, for in the midst of an ongoing process the established form of the past meets the undetermined of the present in a continually emerging creative synthesis.

It is interesting to note that St. Augustine bypassed the conventional form of the problem of "freedom versus determinism" with his extraordinary notion of the different orders of time: past and future time on the one hand, and present time, on the other.[15] The past comprises the processes of recollection (*memoria*) and the future the processes of prediction (*exspectatio*). St. Augustine emphasized that present time, however, is a variable "moment," which may be distended or shrunk. He called this "contuition" (*contuitus*). Past events are now determined and future events are even now determinate. The present moment does not fall within the order of clock time and is thus outside of the causal order. Thus it is experienced not as sequence but as spontaneity.

If one considers the medical specialty of epidemiology, which concerns itself with the study of the distribution of disease and a search for the determinants of the noted distribution, much will be said about cause and effect. One would think that in this kind of science, a rigid devotion to cause and effect would be emphasized. This is not true. In textbooks of epidemiology authors stress that all descriptive sciences take note that certain events tend to be associated with each other in time. Some of these associations between events have characteristics which lead investigators to speak of the relationship as cause and effect—the first event being denoted the *cause* of the second. The use of these words sometimes leads to the idea that the second event is the inevitable consequence of the first, but most schools of philosophy now discredit this concept. The first doubts are usually ascribed to David Hume (1739), who wrote: "We are never able, in a single instance, to discover any power or necessary connection, any quality which binds the effect to the cause, and renders the one an infallible consequence of the other. We only find that one does actually, in fact, follow the other."

Hume's *A Treatise of Human Nature* is regarded by many as the best philosophical work in the English language. Book I of the *Treatise* concerns itself with Hume's thesis that the notion of causality cannot be empirically validated. Although one may note contiguity between two events, the fundamental notion of causality, i.e. necessary connection, is never actually seen in the data but is rather our interpretation of our observations. Thus, science notes observable regularities and correlations but it never notes causes. Science, according to Hume, is not the search for the true cause of events, but for the best available probable predictions about the course of nature founded on correlations of constant conjunctions of events and the psychological habits of human beings.

CHOICE AND RESPONSIBILITY

RESPONSIBLE FREEDOM

Since man does choose and does exercise considerable freedom in many areas of life, although a multitude of factors influence his choices, our society is in desperate need of a concept of responsible freedom. Recent controversies over the separation of church and state, as regarding our public school system, have introduced into the interpretation of the Constitution a very legalistic and narrow point of view. It is obvious that an extreme interpretation of separatism will also make for an extreme secularization of our society. In the long run, then, society may lose more in the way of freedom than it has gained. I realize that this insistence on the separation of church and state to the extent of not even permitting a prayer to be said in school is looked upon as a defensive necessity by certain groups. The sociologist Will Herberg points out that this attitude may be traced to the conviction, widely held though rarely articulated, that because certain minority groups achieved emancipation with the secularization of society, a member of such a group can preserve his free and equal status only so long as culture and society remain secular. The thinking of such a person is that if religion gains a significant place in the everyday life of a community, and if he happens to be outside the bounds of the dominant religion, he will be relegated to the margins of society, displaced, disfranchised culturally if not politically, shorn of his rights and opportunities. The intrusion of religion into education and public life, then would weaken the wall of separation between religion and the state. "The most elementary defensive strategy would thus seem to dictate keeping religion out of education and public life at all costs."[7]

Fromm, in many of his writings, and especially in the book, *Escape From Freedom*, has shown us how man gradually broke his primary bonds with nature and developed

29

his extreme individuality and freedom.[6] Fromm goes on to show how with freedom and individuality, man found himself isolated, alone, anxious, and frightened. His escapes from freedom, then, have involved various types of social alignments including Fascism and Nazism. Fromm stresses that a responsible type of freedom helps the individual develop into an altruistic, giving person who unites himself with the world in the spontaneity of love and productive work. He no longer then feels alone and isolated, but finds himself a part of the solidarity of community which imposes upon him both freedom and responsibility.

Viktor Frankl, both in the therapeutic field and in the report of his own inner consciousness in *From Death Camp to Existentialism*, has challenged us to consider responsibility as the core of man's health.[4] In Frankl's sense, responsibility involves sensing that one has an ineradicable place in some human association—some person, some professional task toward whom he, alone of all the people in the world is relevant. Or, as was true of Frankl's wife, that there is a person whose presence is with one, no matter what happens.

Bondage to authority has destroyed the freedom of many creative persons. By opening this subject, rebellion is not being recommended as an answer within itself.

Dr. Bayard T. Horton of the Mayo Clinic tells an interesting story from his own experience of how authority can stifle the freedom of creativity.[10] In 1926 he began work with Dr. H. Milton Conner of the Mayo Clinic on a medical service housed in the Kahler Hospital. The clinical research which was in progress was not of great interest to Dr. Horton, but he was impressed by the sincerity of Dr. Conner's efforts. With Dr. Herbert Griffin of the Mayo Clinic, Dr. Conner had conceived the idea that patients with pernicious anemia could be treated successfully by feeding them large amounts of liver. From 15 to 20 patients with pernicious anemia, besides other patients with various blood dyscrasias, were under observation daily during the months Dr. Horton was on the service. As a physician in specialty training, he observed these patients from day to day, studied the laboratory reports and copied them on the records, and helped Dr. Conner abstract his case reports and tabulate his data. In March, 1926, Dr. Conner presented the results of this study before the Interstate Postgraduate Assembly, which held its spring meeting at St. Mary's Hospital in Rochester, Minn. Dr. Horton attended the meeting and listened to Dr. Conner's report. He had marshalled his facts and presented them in a clear-cut manner. After he had finished speaking, a visiting professor from one of the midwestern universities got up and casually remarked, "Anyone who thinks he can treat pernicious anemia successfully by feeding patients liver must be out of his mind." Dr. Conner was so discouraged by these remarks that he did not publish his observations. The Nobel Prize—which could have been won—was lost. Dr. Horton declares himself an eyewitness of this and wonders how this could have happened at the Mayo Clinic. A few years later, Minot, Murphy, and Whipple were awarded the Nobel Prize for doing this same work.

Every advance in science has been made at the expense of someone's reputation as an authority. A crucial question often asked is how can one be stimulated by authority and not paralyzed by it.

The relation between freedom and authority is part of the anguish of human existence as man is faced by unsought choices thrust at him from every side. One sees this in Plato's discussion of the prison scene between Socrates and Crito, as well as in George Bernard Shaw's play dealing with the trial of St. Joan. Another dimension of the problem is found in the great American novel, *Huckleberry Finn*. Huck Finn agonizes over participating in helping the slave, Jim, escape although his act brought him in direct conflict with his value system, not abstractly considered but in terms of his relationship to Miss Watson. He weighed the issue as best he could and stood side by side with Jim and defied the whole structure of his life. He had discovered that the tension between freedom and authority was real and that the categories of right and wrong which had seemed so certain and simple were more complex, more involved than he had ever imagined. Huck Finn had, as Socrates and Joan, affirmed the truth that one recognizes the meaning of freedom and authority in the situation where not one or the other, but both, are called into question.

Herein lies the pain of human existence. Decision drives one into the act, and the act sharpens rather than resolves the tension out of which it grows. If authority crushes down freedom, it must lift freedom up again.

DETERMINED AND FREE

The physician's work with patients furnishes him with ample material to have a first hand opinion on this difficult subject. I see many patients who are in bondage and others who are relatively free. The issue must be seen in relationship to a particular individual's particular circumstance. No one is completely free and no one is in complete bondage. It is obvious that many influences from the past of which we are conscious impinge upon our decision-making and behavior. Also there are many determinants of behavior hidden away in the deeper levels of awareness, not readily available to our conscious minds. Then the future, with its hopes and fears, colors our thoughts and activities today.

If one is only a tethered animal, how can he talk about mending his life or improving his relationships? There would be no reason to talk about ethics at all, if the individual is not free to choose between right and wrong. Of course, there is never complete freedom, but without considerable freedom, ethics would be meaningless.

The self is in its own nature a purposive mover although conditioned by past events and experiences. Thus the self is both determined and free—in itself free and creative but limited by the presence of other individuals and factors such as past experiences or future expectations. A belief in complete freedom of the will or strict determinism does not make sense.

From the standpoint of helping an individual bring about change in himself, one must focus on that specific individual and not on abstractions related to freedom of choice. This is so because one person may have the freedom to choose and another may have lost it. The urgency in the biblical message relates to the point of no return if the individual hesitates too long in choosing. The prophetic voice cries out to the individual to wake up and see when he stands at a fork in the road and decide which road to take. Otherwise, he may become aware of the choice only at a point when it is too late for him to make a decision. Typical of such an admonition are the words of Moses, speaking for the Lord: "I call heaven and earth to witness against you this day, that I have set before you life and death, blessing and curse; therefore, choose life, that you and your descendants may live." (Deuteronomy 30:19, RSV).

In the average individual contradictory inclinations are so balanced that choice can be made. There are individuals, however, who appear to have lost the capacity for choosing good and others for choosing evil. Both are determined to act as they do because the balance of forces in their character leaves them no alternative. Such a character structure could be changed, however, under the right circumstances or with the proper techniques.

WHO IS RESPONSIBLE FOR THE IRRESPONSIBLE

I did a psychiatric evaluation on an 8-year-old boy in a correctional school. He had shot and killed his aunt and uncle with whom he lived. His parents had died a year or two before this incident.

The boy reported that his aunt and uncle had often punished him and at times threatened to kill him. Each time

33

he did wrong in their sight, he expected that they would visit the ultimate punishment upon him. One day, he disobeyed his aunt and she beat him harshly. He went into the house, found a small calibre rifle which he had never fired before, loaded it and shot his aunt while she swept the yard. On being asked what he did then, he replied, "She was dead, so I covered her face with a towel and left her in the yard."

He told of how fear swept over him as he awaited the arrival of his uncle from work that evening. He hid in the pantry with the rifle in his hand, expecting his uncle to kill him.

As soon as the uncle arrived home he came into the kitchen to get his supper. He heard a noise in the pantry, and he shouted out, "Who is there?" At that moment the boy shot him. As he fell, the boy reported, his uncle cried out, "Lord, have mercy on me."

Psychological and psychiatric studies revealed an essentially normal boy except for this day of homicide. He spoke gently of his terrible fear of being killed and how each new threat from his uncle or aunt brought his death that much closer. Finally, he decided that it was a matter of killing or being killed, so he decided to strike first.

What are the moral and legal issues regarding the act of this young boy? How great is his responsibility? What is society's responsibility? Although the reader will have his own answers to these questions, some comments are in order before reporting a case which adds other dimensions to the questions asked.

The 8-year-old boy is placed in a special category of responsibility because of his age. Although not held accountable for his actions in the legal sense, this type of offender is usually placed in a correctional institution for diagnostic studies and treatment. It is exceedingly rare for a young child to kill a person intentionally. The notion is not tenable that a capricious element of personality explodes in impulsive violence. A credible position to hold with the 8-year-old murderer described here, consonant with contemporary views of purposiveness, is that his aggression was an adaptive function, namely, to achieve security in the presence of extreme threat and frustration. Since studies indicated no detectable psychological abnormality in the child, the question of illness was not a factor in assigning responsibility. The discovery of illness in such a child would probably be a comfort in that it would help explain why the child killed. It seems obvious that the pathological family situation played a major part in this child's delinquent behavior. In evaluating delinquent behavior, one must study not only the offender but his family and community to explore every possible facet of causality. In social as well as physical illness a crucial question is: What do these symptoms tell us about this individual, his family, and his community? Society surely has a responsibility in rehabilitation and accepts this responsibility at least theoretically. Often the offender is confused, however, by society's ambivalence or hypocrisy in the matter, for the promise to help him frequently means punishment under the guise of rehabilitation. Such a duplicity may promote rather than modify delinquent behavior.

A totally different question of responsibility is introduced by the behavior of a woman in her early thirties who took desperate action against her lover. The woman was going with a man who was separated from his wife. Finally this man decided to go back with his wife and informed his sweetheart of his intention. She was displeased with this decision and felt that she had been wronged and taken advantage of by this man.

One afternoon she sat in her car outside his place of work, waiting for him to come out of the building. When he came out, she ran over him with her car and then drove the car frantically backward and forward over his body. She almost denuded him of skin. He died the following day.

As she waited for him that afternoon she was reading the Bible. She reported, "God and I decided that such men should not be allowed to live."

On examination she was found to be mentally ill. Again one raises the question as to what extent was she responsible for her actions. What was society's responsibility to her?

35

Responsibility for her actions must be assessed in the light of her illness. For many long years society has sought an acceptable solution to the grave problems raised by the mentally ill who commit crimes. A review of this struggle regarding responsibility is given briefly.

One of the great achievements of the church has been its deep and clear appreciation of the nature of moral responsibility. The church has had considerable influence on our legal concepts. Against the primitive view that morality is simply a method of social control concerned solely with overt acts, the Judeo-Christian tradition has insisted that the state of mind and intention from which the act flows—what criminal lawyers called the *mens rea*—is, at the least, morally relevant in a very important way. Even from the days of the Mosaic Law there existed a manifest distinction between a crime with intent and a slaying done unintentionally. The biblical record contains this story: "And this is the case of the slayer, which shall flee thither, that he may live: Whoso killeth his neighbor ignorantly, whom he hated not in time past; as when a man goeth into the wood with his neighbor to hew wood, and his hand fetcheth a stroke with the axe to cut down a tree, and the head slippeth from the helve, and lighteth upon his neighbor that he die, he shall flee unto one of those cities, and live; Lest the avenger of the blood pursue the slayer, while his heart is hot, and overtake him, because the way is long, and slay him; whereas he was not worthy of death, inasmuch as he hated him not in time past." (Deuteronomy 19:4–6).

Out of the ancient doctrine of *mens rea*—of criminal intent—has evolved the modern principle of diminished responsibility of the mentally ill. The historical background of *mens rea*, as the requisite mental element without which there can be no crime, condenses within itself the long history of an important aspect of civilized morality, ethics, philosophy, and religion.

The principle of diminished responsibility because of mental illness is quite compatible with an outgrowth of the true implications of *mens rea*. There must exist innumerable degrees of any particular criminal intent. An enlightened point of view would be to arrive at a legal spectrum of an infinitely graduated scale of responsibility which corresponds, or could be made to correspond closely, to the psychological reality of human beings as understood by present-day medical psychology.

Modern dynamic psychiatry and psychology do not support the legal fiction of an absolute dichotomous distinction between the responsible and the irresponsible. With the development of the legal doctrine of diminished responsibility, for the first time it has become possible to utilize intelligently the central truth of psychiatry—that all human behavior, be it mentally sick or healthy, good or evil, based upon love or upon hate, is distributed upon an infinite spectrum of fine gradation. Karl Menninger has emphasized this in many of his writings and especially in his book *The Vital Balance*.[14]

The term mental illness continues in use although there are many voices in psychiatry and psychology who protest that no type of deviant psychological behavior is a mental disease, that there is no analogy between disease of the body and disease of the mind or emotions, and that the terms "disease" and "illness" should not be applied even to the conceptualization of psychological abnormality. (A major voice in this area is that of Thomas Szasz[19] in such writing as *The Myth of Mental Illness*.) Although this view is logical in many ways, it is unlikely that any sizable proportion of psychiatrists and psychologists agrees with it. Such abnormalities as are manifested by disorder of mind, emotion, character, or behavior can correctly be considered illnesses in a sense analogous to the use of the term in describing the illness of the body. This view can be held without adding confusion or delay in the treatment and healing of these abnormalities. Yet, from the standpoint of the law, these diagnostic categories of mental illness pose a serious dilemma. Severely psychotic people with hallucinatory and delusional ideation can be recognized immediately as having mental diseases and the degree of responsibility readily determined. However, those with character disorders and borderline states such as mild ambulatory schizophrenia are usually held by the courts as responsible for their crimes, but under a strict interpretation of mental disease could possibly be acquitted on the ground of mental illness. The concept of the degree of responsibility would, however, cover this group and protect both society and the defendant.

There is widespread concern throughout our country over the lack of treatment and efforts toward rehabilitation among most of our prison population. Even when an offender is convicted with diminished or limited responsibility because of mental illness and officially labeled as sick and in need of treatment by the courts, he still may not get treatment. The correctional institution to which he is confined can no longer evade the moral and legal responsibility for providing such treatment and rehabilitation, but for the average such defendant today his institution will fail him.

Actually, the treatment principle should be extended to all prisoners—sane, insane, fully-responsible, and partially responsible—each according to need. Two major principles should guide our prison programs: what will insure the maximum rehabilitation of each prisoner, and what will furnish the greatest protection to society against crime. Society's responsibility in these matters cannot be evaded.

Many courts today use "the knowledge of right and wrong" as the test of criminal responsibility. In other words, if it is established that the defendant can distinguish between right and wrong he is held fully responsible. This is the so-called M'Naghten rule which dates back to the famous M'Naghten case.

In 1843 Daniel M'Naghten was tried at the Old Bailey Criminal Court for the wilful murder of Edward Drummond, who was the private secretary of Sir Robert Peel. For years M'Naghten had suffered from delusions of persecution. He had attempted to escape from his imagined persecutors by leaving Scotland and going to England or to France. On numerous occasions he had complained to his father and to various public officials. He became increasingly embittered and decided to right his imaginary wrongs by killing Sir

Robert Peel. With this purpose in mind, he watched Peel's house. Seeing Drummond come out of the house, he followed and shot him in the belief that he was shooting Peel.

The medical testimony was unanimous that M'Naghten was insane, and Justice Tindal appropriately directed a verdict of not guilty by reason of insanity and committed him to an institution for the criminally insane. Within days, public protests over the verdict led to a parliamentary investigation, and the judges retreated under political pressure to the medieval formula of a knowledge of good and evil as a test of criminal responsibility. Since then the M'Naghten rule for criminal responsibility came to be expressed in the following two propositions in order to justify conviction: 1) the accused must know the nature and quality of his act, and 2) he must know that his act is "wrong."

Through the years the majority of the states have stuck by the M'Naghten rule as a test of responsibility in law for acts done. There have been some additions and advances such as the irresistible impulse rule, the New Hampshire rule, the Durham rule, and in 1961, the Currens rule. By far the best approach, however, is the one of limited or diminished responsibility because it takes into consideration criminal intent. The roots of this concept go back to ancient days and its wisdom has survived the centuries.

HELPING THE IRRESPONSIBLE BECOME RESPONSIBLE

The evergrowing body of scientific knowledge about deviant behavior no longer permits a neat and clear-cut division of the responsible from the nonresponsible. This is so because modern science with its new diagnostic instruments has accumulated a vast amount of information indicating that a very large proportion of criminal offenders are sick people. Much of this evidence is not convincing to those preoccupied with moral judgment and vengeful retribution. It is hoped that soon this evidence may become so convincing that the most conservative thinkers will have to accept its validity. Critics of rehabilitation have correctly pointed out that even if the criminal is recognized as mentally sick, that it does not follow that medical science will be able, by itself, to cure successfully or to control this sickness. New types of treatment centers, involving highly trained specialists from a variety of disciplines, are being developed where mentally sick criminals can be adequately cared for with due regard to the protection of society.

In the light of present inadequacies in the treatment and rehabilitation of criminals and juvenile offenders, authorities in legal medicine and forensic psychiatry are busy drawing up blueprints for research, training, and treatment programs involving offenders.

Punishment as a technique of rehabilitation deserves special attention. Criminologists point out that in spite of their efforts to the contrary, criminal law is still framed chiefly in terms of punishing the vicious will.

An institutional program devoted to harsh treatment and repression has accomplished essentially nothing in the rehabilitation of inmates, although such programs have been tried for many weary centuries. Critics of progressive practices often point out that these practices do not work; and they usually don't, if they are not adequately implemented.

Most juvenile courts in our country are woefully lacking in staff to carry out a realistic program of rehabilitation. Usually there is no diagnostic service available to the judge; and the probation staff is insufficient in number and untrained to supervise adequately the youth whom the judge places on probation. Although interested in sound procedures, the court is not able to do what seems to be indicated in each case. Frequently the only recourse is commitment to an institution which, in the majority of cases, is neither necessary nor desirable.

In communities where good programs exist in the courts as well as in the correctional institutions, success in rehabilitation is much greater. For example, a decade ago, about 50 percent of those discharged from state correctional institutions were coming back after getting into new difficulties or progressing to state prisons. Today, in institutions with progressive programs, 85 percent treated make good on parole and lead respectable lives.

Possibly those who advocate harsh treatment for offenders should ponder the words of psychiatrist A. A. Brill: "Punishment, as it is presently applied, is only a deterrent to those who rarely attract it, and it is not a deterrent to those who are continuously subjected to it."

Some interesting results with delinquents have been obtained by probation officers through the use of behavior modification techniques.[20] These represent the systematic application of a reinforcement learning theory largely developed by B. F. Skinner and his associates. The basic premise is: *Behavior is governed by its consequences.* The goal of modifying behavior is attained by altering consequences. Part of the treatment technique involves the determination of these consequences (called *reinforcers*) and applying them when a desired behavior is approximated. An individual's reinforcers can be determined by carefully observing his behavior and by inquiry.

There are two general types of reinforcement. The first is a "positive schedule of reinforcement," and is characterized by such reinforcers as praise, attention, privileges, money, food, use of the car, and so on. Changes in behavior motivated by this positive schedule tend to be relatively rapid and durable. The second is an "aversive schedule of reinforcement," and is characterized by such reinforcers as threats, physical punishment, withdrawal of rewards and privileges, ridicule, and so on. Behavior changes promoted on the latter kind of schedule tend to be relatively limited and temporary.

Actually, the type of schedule used to modify behavior is usually mixed, that is, both positive and aversive. Many delinquents and predelinquents are being raised primarily on an aversive schedule; and, unfortunately, the steps usually taken by public agencies to correct such behavior are likely to be aversive—for example, being expelled from school or incarcerated. The challenge in behavior modification is to use a more balanced schedule of reinforcement.

In effective treatment programs using operant techniques, probation officers make use of their aversive controls, which can temporarily reduce misbehavior, and then build a treatment or rehabilitation plan around positive controls that would teach new socially acceptable behaviors.

In the search for new knowledge and more successful programs of correction, the greatest present need is to make more effective use of the people, the programs, and the skills which are already available.[16] Correctional officials, as well as society in general, have been lacking in the willingness or resourcefulness to incorporate in correctional programs the great body of knowledge already available concerning human behavior, personality development, and the correction of criminal conduct.

The First Congress of Corrections in 1870 formulated a "Statement of Twenty-Two Principles." Much of this farsighted program adopted a century ago by the American Prison Congress still remains to be applied. A listing of a few of these principles will confirm this:[16]

1. Reformation, not vindictive suffering, should be the purpose of penal treatment of prisoners.

2. The prisoner should be made to realize that his destiny is in his own hands.

3. Prison discipline should be such as to gain the will of the prisoner and conserve his self-respect.

4. The aim of the prison should be to make industrious free men rather than orderly and obedient prisoners.

On September 10, 1965, President Johnson signed into law the Prisoner Rehabilitation Act of 1965 (Public Law 89–176). It has been described as the most important legislation affecting the federal prison system in the past several decades.

The law contains three major provisions: (1) It gives the Attorney General the authority to commit or transfer

42

prisoners to residential community treatment centers, commonly called halfway houses. These treatment centers are similar to the halfway houses which have been established in many cities for youthful offenders. (2) The Attorney General can grant brief periods of home leave under emergency conditions or for purposes related to release preparations. (3) The Attorney General can permit prisoners to work in private employment or to participate in programs of community training while continuing as inmates in the institution to which they have been committed. The usual pattern is for the prisoners to take the training during the daytime and return to the prison at night.

Many states and communities have begun to institute similar procedures to those of the Federal Government for the rehabilitation of prisoners. Such procedures help to provide the needed additional latitude in dealing with salvageable convicted offenders. Also the Federal proposals reflect the growing trend in the correctional field to augment inherently limited institutional resources with potentially greater community resources.

The increasing efforts to comprehend the nature of the criminal and experimental approaches in his rehabilitation are bringing increased optimism to the field of corrections. There will be more programs of group counseling in prisons, an expansion of supervised probation opportunities to an increasing number of offenders, an extension of minimum security units for prison and reformatory inmates, as well as a reduction in the average length of confinement in correctional institutions. The problem of criminals and correction must become part and parcel of the community mental health centers and programs, with heavy emphasis on early case finding and prevention.

The magnitude of the task is great both in prevention and rehabilitation. Present resources and methods in most areas are not adequate and appropriate for the task of rehabilitation. Thus, in working toward a brighter future, a hierarchy of tasks must be established.[17] The foremost task is that of prevention. Social and behavioral scientists already know a great deal about the etiology and epidemiology of crime and the criminal, and hence about prevention. The problem as well as the techniques of prevention must be brought insistently and persuasively to the attention of the public.

The second major task is humanizing the correction procedures themselves. Lengthy sentences, regimentation, the removal of all symbols of individuality including definitive sexual activity, and boredom are the hallmarks of traditional correctional institutions. These traditional procedures have been conclusively demonstrated to cripple or destroy man's sense of worth and dignity, without which there can be no healing or rehabilitation.

The third task is to bring the prison, as well as the mental hospital, back into the community. Banishment and ostracism are savage punishments within themselves which push the dehumanization process. The community is a rich resource within itself, as well as a locale in which resources can be mobilized for the rehabilitation of the offender and the mental patient.

REFERENCES

1. Ayer, J. C. A Source Book for Ancient Church History. New York, Scribner, 1939, p. 475.
2. Brenner, C. An Elementary Textbook of Psychoanalysis. New York, International Universities Press, 1955.
3. Einstein, A. The World As I See It. (Trans. by Alan Harris.) New York, Coviei, Friede, 1934, p. 238.
4. Frankl, V. From Death Camp to Existentialism. Boston, The Beacon Press, 1959.
5. Freud, S. The Psychopathology of Everyday Life. (Trans. by A. A. Brill.) New York, The New American Library, 1951.
6. Fromm, E. Escape From Freedom. New York, Rinehart and Co., 1941.
7. Herberg, W. Protestant—Catholic—Jew. Garden City, N.Y., Anchor Books, Doubleday and Co., Inc., 1955, pp. 238–239.
8. Hoffman, M. The idea of freedom in psychoanalysis. Int. J. Psychoanal., 45:579, 1964.

9. Horney, K. New Ways in Psychoanalysis. New York, W. W. Norton and Co., 1939, p. 18.
10. Horton, B. T. The Nobel Prize—won and lost. Headache, Vol. 2, No. 1, April 1962.
11. Jung, C. G. Two Essays on Analytical Psychology. (Trans. by R. F. C. Hull.) New York, Meridian Books, 1956.
12. Knight, R. P. Determinism, freedom, and psychotherapy. In Knight, R. P. and Friedman, C. K., eds. Psychoanalytic Psychiatry and Psychology. New York, International Universities Press, 1954, pp. 365–381.
13. Kubie, L. Freud's legacy to human freedom. Perspect. Biol. Med., 1:105, 1957.
14. Menninger, K. The Vital Balance. New York, Viking Press, 1963.
15. Outler, A. C. Anxiety and grace, an Augustinian perspective. In Hiltner, S. and Menninger, K., eds. Constructive Aspects of Anxiety. New York, Abingdon Press, 1963, pp. 97–98.
16. Satten, J. Barriers to progress in corrections: the high cost of taking science seriously. Proceedings of the Ninety-Third Annual Congress of Corrections of the American Correctional Association, 1963, pp. 23–31.
17. Schimel, J. L. The role of rationality in crime and corrections. In Slovenko, R., ed. Crime, Law and Corrections, Springfield, Ill., Charles C Thomas, Publisher, 1966, pp. 713–716.
18. Slovenko, R., ed. Crime, Law and Corrections. Springfield, Ill., Charles C Thomas, Publisher, 1966.
19. Szasz, T. The Myth of Mental Illness. New York, Basic Books, Inc., 1961.
20. Thorne, G. L., Tharp, Roland G., Wetzel, Ralph J. Behavior modification techniques: new tools for probation officers. Federal Probation, Vol. 31, 1967, pp. 21–27.
21. Zilboorg, G. Sigmund Freud: His Exploration of the Mind of Man. New York, Scribner, 1951.

3

The Level of Awareness

A lawyer came to me asking if he could get some help with a client of his who had killed his wife. In reviewing the situation with the lawyer and his client (now a prisoner) an unusual story unfolded.

This prisoner awoke one morning at about 3 a.m. to find himself with an icepick in his hand, standing over the body of his wife. He called the physician, police, and relatives immediately. His wife was dead from multiple puncture wounds, and he was taken to prison.

This man had been a responsible worker in the community and was respected by everybody. His wife was suspected by many as having an emotional disorder. She was often out late at night in the company of other men. She often threatened her husband and usually awoke him when she came home in the early morning hours.

He had become afraid of her and did not know how to manage the developing crisis. Here was a man who had lost sleep, was fearful for his life, fatigued, and evidently asleep when she approached his bed that night. (The source of the icepick remains a mystery, for there had not been one in his home.) In his first moment of conscious awareness he knew he had stabbed his wife.

What was this man's level of awareness at the time he stabbed her? When he became aware of the threat to his life that night, did he react spontaneously to save himself before he was awake and alert? Had he been so conditioned by the long period of psychological stress that the primitive self-preservation defenses operated unconsciously? These were the questions asked in court, and the answers influenced the court's decision about the prisoner.*

Conscience and consciousness are inseparable, and their interdependence has always been recognized. The Stoics first explored the cognitive aspect of conscience as distinct from the judicial, and recognized that to act with *conscientia*, with knowledge, requires consciousness.[1] Choice and responsibility are at the heart of moral behavior. Thus in any consideration of level of awareness the two basic postulates always present in ethics must be kept in mind: freedom of choice and knowledge of the things between which to choose. The grasp of these will vary in levels of awareness but without them any talk of morality or function of conscience is meaningless.

THE UNCONSCIOUS

Mental states in sickness and health have a broad range of awareness from consciousness to unconsciousness. An exploration of present-day terminology regarding levels of awareness seems indicated.

Motivations frequently spring from causes too deeply

---

* Although legal precedents in similar court cases were not well established or easy to identify, the special factors related to this man's behavior were weighed carefully by the court. The man was found guilty, as one would expect, but was given only a light prison sentence.

seated to be apparent. Also emotional forces within the individual and of which he may be unaware act on him in such a way as to influence his behavior even though he knows nothing about them consciously. Most behavior actually is a constellation of unconscious and conscious motivations. Much of our knowledge concerning motivations has been acquired by the psychoanalytic method of studying the unconscious mind through free association techniques, analysis of dreams, fantasies, slips of the tongue, and so on. Psychotherapy has confirmed and made concrete through an immense amount of material St. Paul's insight in the dependence of our free acts on motives which in the act itself are not consciously present.* Through the analysis of ambiguous motives in the actions of patients, the realism of the doctrine of the "bondage of the will" has been made manifest by the psychotherapist.

A completely satisfactory definition of the unconscious has never been found. Some behavioral scientists feel that instead of speaking of the unconscious, one should emphasize unconscious mental processes. Terminology at this point has been especially confusing for laymen. In psychiatry unconscious has been used with two different and separate meanings. The first meaning has to do with the absence of participation of the perceptive self or conscious ego. Thus when the conscious part of the mind is not functioning, the individual is said to be unconscious. We witness this at a boxing match when the referee does his count-down and gets no response from the prostrate boxer. The second meaning of unconscious refers to a division of the psyche and is the concern of this discussion. The term is further complicated by the use of subconscious as synonymous with unconscious. Mental processes the existence of which are assumed is referred to as the unconscious.

The familiar comparison of the psyche to an iceberg emphasizes the ever changing character of the psyche. The hidden part of the iceberg (most of it) is compared to the

* "I do not understand my own actions. For I do not do what I want, but I do the very thing I hate." (Romans 7:15, RSV).

48

unconscious. The constant moving and rolling with the waves lift new parts of the iceberg above the surface and submerge other parts. The events of life do the same thing with the psyche and lift hidden parts into consciousness and submerge others into unconsciousness.

Actually, if one spoke of levels of awareness in the mind he would have a more easily understood concept than that of conscious and unconscious.

Why did Freud's concept of the unconscious meet considerable resistance from both the scientists and the laymen of fifty years ago? It indicated that a man was really not as much his own master as he had considered himself and many of the forces motivating him originated and operated in a manner of which he had little direct control or knowledge. The acceptance of such a concept then (and possibly now) was a painful blow to the self-esteem of the average person. Other factors are involved also in making an understanding of the unconscious difficult. A constant vigilance or censoring mechanism is maintained by forces in the psyche to prevent certain unconscious material from entering into conscious awareness.

Different principles of operation are revealed by the mental qualities of the conscious and unconscious. One example is the proud and laborious way man has built his ability to think logically. In the unconscious, however, logic does not hold sway over the mental activities. Impulses striving in opposite directions can coexist in a way that would be thoroughly unacceptable to the conscious mind. Another difference is the passage of time which gradually diminishes the importance and clarity of events. In the unconscious, time does not exist, so that repressed memories can retain their original strength for years.

Hypnosis is dramatic and convincing evidence of the existence of the unconscious. It is quite easy to implant into the mind of a hypnotized subject ideas which will remain beneath his awareness in the waking state and yet be capable of exerting influence. This can be demonstrated, for example, by having the hypnotist tell the subject who is in a trance that within minutes after awakening he will feel very warm and will open the window to let in fresh, cool air. Shortly after awakening, he will open the window. If for some reason he is unable to carry out the act suggested, he will become very tense, and the act will be performed on the first opportunity. The explanation for such a phenomenon lies in the fact that the hypnotist has implanted in the unconscious of the subject the urge to open the window. It remains there pressing for discharge and also producing tension as long as it is ungratified.

Slips of the tongue are a frequent and common demonstration of the unconscious by bringing to the surface the existence of unrecognized feelings in the deeper layers of the mind which are pressing for discharge. Such feelings though not strong enough to overcome resistance and reach consciousness, are capable of changing a word or a phrase in a statement so as to alter its entire meaning.[2]

A patient in an interview may be referring to his wife and slip and call her his mother. A person may be saying good-bye to his guest and very politely say, "Please don't come back again." The story is told of a student who took his mother to see the trophy room of his university where the boar's head was kept. He threw open the door and said, "Mother, here is where we keep the whore's bed."

UNCONSCIOUS CONDITIONING
AND FORCIBLE INDOCTRINATION

Any discussion of conditioning should begin with the work of the Russian Nobel Prize winner, Ivan Petrovich Pavlov. Physiologist Pavlov has long been discussed in medical and physiological circles because of certain of his experiments which led to the introduction of the term "conditioned reflex."[7] Pavlov experimented on dogs by placing small tubes in the salivary glands in the dogs' mouths and also in their stomachs with the object of measuring the amount of fluids aiding digestion which was produced by both the salivary glands and those glands in the lining of the stomach.

Pavlov knew that salivation was associated with eating and that if the dogs were hungry, their mouths would water each time they saw food. He took advantage of this inborn response to develop in his experimental animal the salivating response in answer to a stimulus which would not ordinarily create it. As he would bring into the dog's presence a meal, an assistant would simultaneously ring a bell. He continued to repeat this sequence of events for some time. The sight of the food made the dog anticipate the meal, and the digestive juices were poured out from its salivary glands and its stomach. After many repetitions of the combined food-bell stimulus, Pavlov rang the bell but did not give the dog the meal. The dog reacted to the bell alone just as it had previously reacted to the sight of food. The digestive juices were poured out in abundance. Thus, he discovered that the dog could be induced to salivate involuntarily in response to an arbitrary signal. The animal had been "conditioned" to respond to the ringing of the bell as if that sound were both the smell and taste of food.

Pavlov did this work early in the century. Later his experiments on conditioned reflex were taken to a further stage. His later work, however, did not become well known until almost the beginning of the Second World War. Certain students of brainwashing and thought control have discussed the relevance of Pavlov's findings to some of the totalitarian political conditioning that is going on in the world today.[6,8]

A knowledge of Pavlov's experimental work is illuminating in understanding how modifications in behavior can be brought about by stress. Dogs, like human beings, respond to stresses or conflict situations according to their different types of inherited temperament. A dog's reactions to normal stress depend on both its inherited constitution and on environmental influences to which it has been exposed. Although these may alter the details of its behavior, they do not change the basic temperamental pattern. Dogs, like human beings, suffer a breakdown when stresses or conflicts become too great for their nervous system to master. At the point of breakdown, their behavior shows signs of varying from that normally characteristic of their inherited temperamental type and previous conditioning. The amount of stress or conflict that a dog can tolerate without breaking down varies with its physical condition. Fatigue, fevers, drugs, and glandular changes can all lower resistance. When the nervous system has for long periods been stimulated beyond its capacity to respond normally, a dog's responses eventually become inhibited, no matter what its temperamental type may be. This inhibition is protective and results in altered behavior on the dog. Three distinguishable phases of increasingly abnormal behavior which occur are: (1) that phase in which the brain gives the same response to both strong and weak stimuli; (2) the phase in which the brain responds more actively to weak stimuli than to strong; (3) the phase in which conditioned responses and behavior patterns turn from positive to negative or from negative to positive.

A crucial event in the career of Pavlov was the Leningrad flood in 1924. The Leningrad flood gave him the clue as to how the brain might be wiped almost clean, at least temporarily, of all the conditioned behavior patterns recently implanted in it. He had implanted a whole set of positive conditioned behavior patterns in a group of dogs. These dogs were accidentally trapped by flood water which flowed in under the laboratory door and rose gradually until the dogs were swimming around in terror with heads at the top of their cages. At almost the last moment for rescue, a laboratory attendant rushed in, pulled them down through the water, and opened their cage doors to safety. This terrifying experience made some of the dogs switch from a state of acute excitement to one of severe inhibition. On retesting them afterward, Pavlov found that the recently implanted conditioned responses had all disappeared. Other dogs, which had faced the same ordeal merely by registering increased excitement, were not similarly affected, and the implanted behavior patterns had persisted. Pavlov followed up this clue and found that in addition to the abnormalities induced by lesser degrees of protective inhibition, lay a further degree of inhibitory activity capable of disrupting for the time being all recently implanted conditioned responses. Most of the dogs which had reached this stage could later on have their old conditioned behavior pattern restored, but this would take months of patient work. Even a trickle of water running under the door of the laboratory would affect profoundly the dogs who had had their patterns abolished.

An American psychiatrist, Robert Jay Lifton, has reported on some of the historical applications of Pavlov's discoveries* in his observations and research in thought reform.[5] Lifton spent nearly two years in Hong Kong conducting a psychiatric investigation of thought reform by means of interviews with people who had been put through the process in China. He gives numerous cases of Western civilians who

---

* Some contend that the fiendish practice of forcible indoctrination, or brainwashing, is not as much an outgrowth of Pavlovian psychology as is claimed today; rather, the Russian methods, for example, have grown directly out of centuries-old traditions of a secret state police, which has had generations of trial and error to develop ways of breaking men for political reasons.[9] The old methods of transforming the victim into someone who is weak and has no convictions focus on regression to bring about the childish state. The techniques for inducing regression involve anxiety and terror, isolation, prevention of sleep, semi-starvation, heterosexual frustration, and treatment of prisoners in a deliberately infantilizing way. Such techniques, usually applied simultaneously, create a powerful pressure to slip back into an infantile condition characterized by a state of emotional dependence on others, suggestibility, and dreamy inability to distinguish between reality and fantasy. It is remarkable that many men have been able to fight these undertows successfully, and either remain silent or actively defy or deceive their captors. Others, as weak as these are strong, succumb entirely and develop psychoses. The indoctrinator fails, however, if he drives his man crazy. He must gauge his pressure carefully and push the prisoner almost to the breaking point but not quite over it. The near-psychotic, extreme condition cannot be maintained for many days, but is usually effective in cracking resistance, bringing about a preliminary "confession," and the development of an attitude of defeat and despair.

went through the experience of arrest, confession, "reeducation," and expulsion from China, as well as their experience after returning to their homelands.

He also describes a group of Chinese intellectuals who had undergone thought reform in regular universities or in special "revolutionary universities" and examines the historical and cultural currents acting upon each man's personal response.

The author also applies his criteria of totalism to the agencies of human change and suggests as an alternative to thought reform, an open form of personal change. His findings have profound relevance for any student of human behavior. Lifton points out that the great agencies of human change—educational, psychological, religious, and political—make use of four general approaches to changing people: coercion, exhortation, therapy, and realization. Ideological totalism utilizes all four, but it leans most heavily upon the first two.

Lifton describes the message of coercion as that of "You must change and become what we tell you to become—or else." The goal of this type of naked coercion is to produce a cowed and demoralized follower. It is directed at the most primitive of human emotions and stimulates the desire for flight or fight, or to freeze and fear, or submit completely.

The exhortative approach is "You should change—if you are a moral man—and become what we (and the name of a higher moral authority) tell you to become." Exhortation seeks to create converts and disciples of the people who have been changed in accordance with the specific ideological convictions of the exhorter. The appeal is to the individual's wish to be a good man or to become a better one. It capitalizes on preexisting tendencies toward experience in guilt and shame, including existential guilt. Lifton portrays beautifully how the Chinese showed some of the prisoners how far short they had fallen of the goals they had set for themselves and of their own potentialities and also how far from ideal had been many of their interpersonal relationships. Thus the very core of existential guilt was focused on by

54

these thought reform specialists. Lifton goes on to say that this is the method par excellence of religions and of pseudo-religious secular ideologies, both of which enforce their moral appeal by the promise of reward, earthly or supernatural. Lifton designates exhortation as the most prominent of thought reform approaches.

The therapeutic approach is: "You can change—from your sickly state, and find relief for your suffering—if you have a genuine urge to become healthy, and if you are willing to follow my (or our) method and guidance." Its goal is physical and emotional health and freedom from incapacitating disease and defect. It makes its appeal to that part of a man that is most reasonable, health-seeking, and balanced. The medical profession has always used this approach, and in the emotional sphere it is best exemplified by psychotherapy and psychoanalysis. Lifton points out that religious and secular ideologies also use this approach or at least make claims on it. Thought reform frequently refers to illness, health, and cure. The usage implies biological restoration, and places reformers in the role of social physicians.

The message of realization is described as: "You can change—in such a fashion that you will be able to express more fully your own potential—if you are willing to confront yourself with ideas and approaches which challenge your present ways of knowing and acting." Lifton describes succinctly the possibilities and hazards of this fourth approach in seeking to bring about change in people. Its aim is to produce a person who expresses his creative potential fully and who extends his faculties to the utmost in producing the highest level at which he is capable. Although this goal is closely related to that of the therapeutic approach, it is not the same. It may cause rather than relieve pain, and may promote within a person periods of incapacity alternating with creative peaks instead of a continuity of health and strength.

Lifton contends that no one of the approaches ever appears in pure form, and significant attempts at changing people usually embody elements of all four.

55

A special word regarding approaches to reeducation as they relate to religion, government, and science. One should take a close look at the prevailing themes within a particular religious milieu. Religious totalism can be recognized, according to Lifton, by the following trends: exaggerated control and manipulation of the individual, blanketing of the milieu with guilt and shame, emphasis upon man's hopeless depravity and worthlessness and upon his need to submit abjectly to a vengeful deity—all within the framework of an exclusive and closed system of ultimate truth. The author contrasts religious totalism with those religious situations which stress man's worth and his potentialities as well as his limitations; his capacity to change as well as the difficulties inherent in bringing about such change; and faith and commitment without the need for either self-negation or condemnation of nonbelievers.

Such attitudes leave room for emotional and intellectual growth and a broadened sensitivity to the world rather than a retreat into religious embeddedness. Since each of the world's major religions, at times in the course of its history, has demonstrated both of these contrasting tendencies, any particular religious environment must be judged according to its own characteristics. Erich Fromm in his book, *Psychoanalysis and Religion,* presents a similar point of view.[3]

Lifton feels that nontotalist approaches to reeducation can encourage an experience of individual change very different from that promoted by thought reform, one characterized by openness to the world rather than by personal closure. Chinese reformers seem to assume an extreme malleability of human nature, whereas staunch believers in a rigid determinism feel that man is so determined by his instincts and by the events of his childhood that all suggestion of later change is illusory. Lifton suggests a middle ground and declares that the capacity for change during adulthood is real and perpetual. There is imaginative expression of this capacity to change in the great mythological theme of death and rebirth, a theme given coercive expression in thought reform. Such a change can occur through more or less formal association with education, religion, therapy, or politics. It also takes place through less structured encounters with new people, new ideas, or new landscapes. The process of change can be envisioned within a three-step sequence: confrontation, reordering, and renewal.

Confrontation represents a combination of inner impulse and external challenge which creates within a person the simultaneous recognition of the need and the possibility for change. Most behavioral scientists believe that there is in man a fundamental urge toward change—a force which propels him in the direction of what is new and unknown—ever battling with his opposing tendency to cling exclusively to what is emotionally familiar. Without such an inner assistance from each individual person, the agencies of change could have little success. Thus, external challenge is always related to internal urges to know and to master. Lifton emphasizes that open confrontation causes a questioning of identity different from thought reform's assault upon identity. The experience calls forth the human faculties of introspection and increased self-consciousness. The person often feels the guilt and shame of unfulfillment, stemming primarily from his failure to utilize his rich potential resources.

One advances from confrontation to the phase of reordering. This means embarking upon the work of reeducation and change. As in thought reform, reordering generally includes a personal "emptying" process—some form of confession and exploration of existential guilt. Past emotional patterns are exposed and explored. When the individual views himself in the harsh light of the realities of his own limitations, he may experience the dread of a true sense of tragedy. The emptying process is accompanied by a corresponding absorption of new or refashioned ideas and emotions in which the person's own past is reinterpreted. One should have the opportunity to test the personal validity of new ideas, to experiment with new forms of human relationships and creative expression, rather than the demand that all of these be subjugated to prefabricated totalist ideology and language. It is obvious that any person in the process of change reinterprets

57

his past with some ideological bias and an over critical attitude conditioned by his urge to change. He does find ways, however, to moderate his judgments through both introspection and outside influences, rather than having them further distorted by an immoderate, guilt-saturated, totalist milieu.

The final stage consists of a sense of open renewal, contrasting with thought reform's closed form of rebirth. The individual views his relationships to old authorities as steps along his personal path toward greater independence. There is an interplay between his concern for who he is and to what he is committing his life. In the wider educational environment he is often able to develop new social identifications and responsibilities that transcend his family, profession, and previous subculture.

Although a person of any age is capable of changing or being changed, Lifton's findings carry a special urgency regarding young people. Youths are the ones who most enthusiastically espouse the change-stimulating ideas and ideologies. Youth groups represent a human vanguard in the sense that they are the first and most intense indicators of the kinds of psychological experience and identity shift which will occur subsequently in adult populations throughout a particular society.

It is quite possible that the developmental phase of late adolescence and early adulthood has special significance for all subsequent personal change. This is a time of major emotional turbulence, great ideological receptivity, and maximum experiential intensity. Many present-day behavioral scientists believe that during any adult change it is necessary to revive in some fashion the predominant patterns of this late adolescent phase of life, probably even more than those of the earlier phases of childhood to which psychology and psychiatry presently direct major attention. This is not to minimize character development in early childhood but to suggest that the altering of adult identity depends upon a specific recapturing of much of the emotional tone which prevailed at the time when this adult identity was formed.

This view is suggested by William James' association

of religious conversion with the "ordinary storm and stress and moulting-time of adolescence," and his conviction that "conversion is in its essence a normal adolescent phenomenon, incidental to the passage from the child's small universe to the wider intellectual and spiritual life of maturity."[4] Thus the "moulting-time" of adolescence establishes within each man a model for later adult change.

IMPLICATIONS OF HUMAN PERSUASION

What does all of this mean for today? One sees a common denominator running through the research of such investigators of thought reform as Pavlov, Sargant, Meerloo, and Lifton. When a person is confronted by stresses of all kinds, when he is fatigued and threatened, when he is filled with conflict and struggling to resolve the conflict, he is a candidate ripe for major changes in his life. In some way, the tablet of the mind softens. The old imprint is wiped away and a new imprint can be stamped there.

If one compares the techniques of thought reform (brainwashing), hypnotic suggestion, and religious conversion, he finds many similarities from the neurophysiological point of view. I hasten to add that there is another dimension to religious conversion not involved in thought reform. This is the recognition of a Power or powers that transcend those of the human mind. The psychological studies of religious revival have often failed to recognize or consider this dimension and have thereby rightfully incurred the criticism of religious leaders for such a neglect.

We had recently an unusual experience in our Tulane University Psychiatric Clinic. A young woman who had been treated in psychotherapy without much result was suddenly and dramatically healed by a faith-healer who cast out the demons from within her. The course of psychotherapeutic treatment, which had by that time extended to ten months, had shown the patient to have a severe emotional disturbance. Not only did she have a character disorder with many hysterical features, but some evidence pointed to a psychotic process.

After the healing, which included five exorcism sessions over a period of one month, the health of the patient was so improved that therapy was no longer necessary. Her symptoms disappeared, and she began to function with mature self-confidence.

She grew up in a hypermoralistic environment and previously had never been able to resolve many conflicted feelings. Her religious faith usually failed her. Now she claimed to have attained a new theology which resolved these conflicts. She now knew, she reported, that God loved her, and she had had the religious experience to prove it.

I listened to tape recordings of several of the healing sessions. The faith-healer who worked with her has a group who sings, chants, and prays as he works with the patient. He addresses each devil by name and carries on a heated conversation with each one. The situation builds up to a fever-pitch of excitement. Finally, the healer and the patient defeat the devils, and she is freed from this bondage to evil spirits. The healing process for her was long and exhaustive.

This faith-healer feels that exorcism and psychotherapy have many similarities, the only real difference being the extent to which the patient is directed and the means by which the psychic problems are symbolically represented.

My examination of the techniques of exorcism, especially as represented in this case history, support the scientific contention that faith-healing, hypnotic suggestion, psychotherapy, and thought reform have some similarities. Each technique, however, has other dimensions and other factors to consider. A question to ponder is precisely what it is that enables one human being to influence another profoundly. Thus, religion is a most appropriate area for behavioral science studies, provided the theological dimensions are not lost through such an approach.

Mankind's experiences with thought reform, both past and present, place upon our shoulders the responsibility of assessing our techniques of teaching, influencing, motivating, and changing. Certain approaches today in advertising represent major assaults upon both the privacy and freedom of man. Thus, the full spectrum of conditioning takes on new meaning in the light of our present knowledge and in relationship to our complex media of communication.

Especially needed is a clear understanding of what it takes to thwart coercive manipulation of human behavior. Studies have shown that people who are not adversely influenced by coercive manipulation show a pattern of ego strength and a firm sense of identity.[5,9,10] A person's identity comprises all that is meant by self, with ramifications into his attitudes, ideology, beliefs and knowledge. It involves his patterns of relationship with other people, particularly the important figures in his family of orientation. An important constituent of a person's identity is his *feeling* of personal continuity, which, if strong, can itself be a bulwark against easy change in his behavior. Identity is also a tie between the most intimate sense of self and enduring structure in the person's environment—his possessions, home, friends, relatives, countrymen, and so on.

The view is widespread that the actions of people can be controlled at will by means of rewards and punishments. Such an interpretation of learning has become the basis for the view that the beliefs and values of individuals can be manipulated arbitrarily, without regard to the content and meaning of the given situation. Society is looked upon as a maze in which one learns the rules of the game by suitable rewards and punishments. If one believes the preceding statement, then it is easy for him to believe that suggestion, imitation, and prestige are the fundamental forces shaping values and opinions. Today, there is rebellion in many people against the concept that men are ruled solely by habit and anticipations of reward and punishment, for there are experiences which bring insight into one's situation. The urgent task is to distinguish, on psychological and religious grounds, experience which furthers understanding and experience which narrows and blinds.

Normal phenomenological experience runs counter to

the notion that people are helpless victims of inexorable circumstances. Most people do not want to believe that they are mere robots, and they do not actually feel that they are. Carl Rogers' remarkable comment points up the difficulty: "I prefer to live with what seems to me to be a genuine paradox, . . . that in our pursuit of science, we are fools if we do not assume that everything that occurs is a portion of a cause-and-effect sequence, and that nothing occurs outside of that. But I also feel that if we adopt that point of view in our living as human beings, in our confrontation with life, then that is death."[10] Rogers' statement epitomizes a rather widespread attitude that the rules of the scientific game are applicable in many situations but in studying real persons in a real world one sees dimensions of human behavior that seem to transcend these rules. Heraclitus' words, written centuries ago, offer both caution and comfort: "You cannot find the boundaries of the soul, even if you travel every road, so deep is the measure of it."

Man's behavior is conditioned not just by his individual and ancestral past but also by his aims, his aspirations, and where he is going, as Jung repeatedly emphasized. Along with instinctual forces, there is constant and often creative development, the search for wholeness, and the yearning for rebirth. It is a distortion of modern psychology to view adult behavior only in terms of infantile motives and biological needs. In analyzing human behavior, one must look into man's past and into man's future. The two views when combined yield a picture of man characterized by hope and something to live for.

Man has a need, not to be blind, but to make some sense out of the happenings around him, to grasp something of the order of things, and to act according to his understanding. Reductionistic concepts give only part of the picture of man. The world around him is full of things which challenge and command his interest and compel him to action. Instead of constant concern with himself, the healthy person is deeply concerned with his surroundings. One of the deepest needs in man is his quest for meaning.

62

THE LEVEL OF AWARENESS

Fortunately, the individual has a need not simply to exploit others but to enter into productive relationships with them. Sharing and playing a part in the life of a group can become a matter of supreme interest. It is the general condition and not the exception that the individual has a need to live with others truthfully and to establish relations of trust, good faith, and cooperation not based solely on the calculation of profit. There is a need to act according to what one perceives as inherently fitting and not simply to follow arbitrary custom. The outcome of the socialization of the individual, or rather the development of his moral stance, is often not the acceptance of some static set of folkways but participation in the moral argument of his time and civilization.

REFERENCES

1. Fletcher, J. Morals and Medicine. Boston, Beacon Press, 1954.
2. Freud, S. Psychopathology of Everyday Life. (Trans. by A. A. Brill.) New York, New American Library, 1951.
3. Fromm E. Psychoanalysis and Religion. New Haven, Yale University Press, 1950.
4. James, W. The Varieties of Religious Experience. New York, The Modern Library, 1929, p. 196.
5. Lifton, R. J. Thought Reform and the Psychology of Totalism: A Study of Brainwashing in China. New York, W. W. Norton and Co., Inc., 1961.
6. Meerloo, J. A. M. The Rape of the Mind: The Psychology of Thought Control, Menticide, and Brainwashing. Cleveland, The World Publishing Co., 1956.
7. Pavlov, I. P. Conditioned Reflexes and Psychiatry. (Trans. by Horsley Gantt.) London, Lawrence and Wishart, 1941.
8. Sargant, W. Battle for the Mind: A Physiology of Conversion and Brainwashing. Garden City, New York, Doubleday and Co., Inc., 1957.
9. Wolff, H. G., and Hinkle, L. E., Jr.: Communist interrogation and indoctrination of enemies of the state. Analysis of methods used by the communist police state. A.M.A. Arch. Neurol. Psychiat. 76:115, 1956.
10. Worchel, P., and Byrne, D. eds. Personality Change. New York, John Wiley & Sons, 1964, pp. 288–318.

4

The Dark Side of Man

Stories based on the history and legends of the Old West retain immense popularity in the United States. Also, through the media of film and the printed page, they have become a pervasive and uniquely American cultural export. They have given rise to sports and games which appeal to both children and adults the world over.

With minor variations, the stereotyped western story is as follows: The cowboy hero and his "sidekick" happen upon strangers in great peril. After fast and furious confrontations with the villain and his henchman through chases, gun battles, or saloon brawls, the cowboy eventually and inevitably triumphs in personal combat over the villain. Declining the grateful offers of those he has saved—a position of respect and authority in the community and/or marriage to the rancher's daughter—he and his companion ride off into the sunset.

As examination of the stereotyped western story, with the aid of psychoanalytic insights, reveals that the ostensible struggle to bring law and order to the frontier serves as a colorful but relatively unimportant facade behind which a far more ancient universal and personal battle rages.[1] This battle is one that every child must wage within himself to master the dark forces that run counter to the most fundamental moral prohibitions.

While the spectator of the western film or the participant in the "Cowboy and Indian" game identifies mainly with the hero, he also surreptitiously identifies with the other members of the cast and thus can give vent, vicariously, to impulses which are foreign to his idealized self-concept. By identifying with the various characters in the story, he can express both his constructive and destructive impulses and in the end see the triumph of the former. The fascination of the western story is that it gives momentary hope, even vicarious realization, that one can prevail not only over external enemies but over internal ones.

On some level, therefore, man is aware of and deeply concerned with his dark and hidden impulses. Early religious teachers held that man was engaged in an inner struggle that he had to resolve. The conflict involved the dichotomy between the *yetzer hara* (the evil inclination) and the *yetzer hatov* (the good instinct).[17] No psychotherapist can work with patients without an appreciation of this struggle in every person he treats.

The dark side of man cannot be discussed without including both theological and psychological dimensions.* The major intention here, however, is to show the clinical relevance of the topic in any study of human behavior. Conrad referred to the elemental wildness in man as a *heart of darkness*.[2] In this smoldering power there are both salvation and damnation.**

* For a recent theological study and survey of the problems of evil, see Hick's *Evil and the Love of God*.[8]

** In Conrad's *Heart of Darkness* and his *The Secret Sharer*, he used the same mythical theme: the theme of initiation and moral education, the theme of progress through temporary reversion and achieved self knowledge, the theme of man's exploratory descent into the primitive sources of his being. Conrad believed that one must know evil and his own capacity for evil before he can be capable of good. Man must descend into the pit before

65

THE ROOTS OF THE ORIGINAL SIN CONCEPT

Nietzsche declared that "God is dead." As proof, he suggested we look at the churches which had become the tombs of God. "He is dead because we human beings had killed him." Nietzsche was referring to the God of traditional religion who had died at the hands of modern day man.[15]

Kierkegaard must have shared Nietzsche's feelings about what was taking place in the churches. After listening to a particular sermon one Sunday, Kierkegaard remarked, "I feel I have been trampled to death by a flock of geese."

Although God be declared dead, one thing seems sure. The human quest for the eternal and the timeless is still with us. Even in the midst of man's humanity, he seems driven to transcend himself by relating his finite existence to the eternal.* For a large segment of modern man, God is dead, but in God's place many idols have been enthroned— the state, science, culture, money, one's profession. These idols have been given religious devotion. Modern man is beginning to learn that whether his idols are made of gold or stone or fashioned of the power strivings of a materialist culture, they are illusory and deceptive. The Hebrew prophets

---

he can see the stars. A price must be paid, however, for any such perilous journeys and descents. One must atone for even a temporary alliance with the powers of darkness. A basic theme of Conrad's is the underlying kinship between all men—saint and sinner.

* When man has failed in his search to find God, he has at times turned to drugs to help him in his quest. Greatly treasured have been those substances or drugs used to bring mortal flesh into the presence of the divine. For example, some have called the hallucinogenic drug LSD a new religion not unconnected with our "God is dead" era. They have gone on to say that the "standard religious brands" have not been delivering the goods. Thus people are turning to technological mysticism, namely psychedelic drugs such as LSD, Psilocybin, and Mescaline.

pointed this out long ago. Our sense of frustration and our chronic state of being at cross-purposes with ourselves and with our fellowman suggest strongly that idols by any name are poor substitutes and do not satisfy man's need for God. The emphasis of existentialism is on the sense of tragedy of modern man, his discontent, and his alienation, which stem from the impasse of his living as if "God is dead," while being unable to fulfill himself as a human being in a world without God. This type of tragedy the psychotherapist encounters almost daily in the lives of people who have no conscious awareness of just what is wrong, but reveal patently in their dreams their isolation and aloneness and their compelling hunger for wholeness and communion with something which is eternal.

A discussion of God and man leads inevitably to a discussion of sin. Today people seem to be afraid of the word sin, and in psychological and psychiatric circles the word guilt is used. Thus when one acts in forbidden ways, this is not referred to as "sinning." A study of history reveals men who believed themselves "sinners" and who feared "hell" was awaiting them but somehow lived with fewer pangs of conscience than people do today. These men made their "peace with God," sometimes as late as on their deathbeds as did Casanova, "I lived as a philosopher and I die as a Christian." Today, modern men seek fulfillment on their own terms and according to their own interpretation; and at the same time manufacture their private hells and torture themselves with guilt complexes and new categories of demons that their predecessors never dreamed of.

Since man attains humanness only by reaching out beyond himself, he cannot fully succeed because he is human and is inextricably and irrevocably bound to and limited by his nature. In the awareness of human limitation, man contemplates his finiteness and begins to see his life in some kind of perspective. It is here that the sense of sin originates, that he begins to comprehend something of a broken relationship. He then realizes the meaning of sin as estrangement from God and not deviation from rules.

The fact of sin constitutes the central problem of the biblical record. The assumption of the universality of sin in the Old and New Testaments does not declare or imply that sin originates from nature. In this respect the biblical view differs from many other doctrines regarding the nature of man. The biblical view declares that sin is not a product of the lowest in man's nature but a product of the misuse of his highest endowment, his capacity for fellowship with God. Sin is contrary to man's true nature and not indigenous. Thus, the concept of sin presupposes a divine-human relationship which had been broken. The story of the Garden of Eden in Genesis and the parable of the prodigal son in Luke illustrate that sin presupposes a tie, a relationship, and results in alienation. (Genesis 3:1–24; Luke 15:11–32).

The problem of the roots of sin, of evil, in human life has been the topic of serious thought and attention throughout the ages. Biblical theology has generally sought to derive sin from man's abuse of the freedom with which he was created. Such an explanation, however, requires an answer to the question of how it is possible for man to misuse his freedom so that he will set himself against God. The doctrine of original sin is the answer usually given. Its substance is that the transgression which caused Adam's fall and expulsion from the Garden of Eden is transmitted from generation to generation so that all of Adam's descendants must be regarded as being of a depraved nature.* The apostle Paul introduced into Christian thinking this interpretation of the fall of Adam. Thus, the doctrine of total depravity has been linked with the theory of original sin in such a way that Adam's sin became determinative for all mankind. (Romans 5:12–21). When Paul taught that as in Adam all men have sinned, so in Christ they are saved, he suggested an interpretation of the Genesis story foreign to Jewish thought

* The psychiatric concept of the id, referring to the basic, unrefined biological impulses, does not differ to any great extent from that aspect of the theological doctrine of original sin, which refers to man's bondage to his primitive impulses, his rebellious nature, and his destructive tendencies.

and furnished Christian theology a central theme. The early church theologians such as Irenaeous and Tertullian, who first adopted this pattern of thought, never bothered to explain how Adam's sin could be transmitted to all of his descendants. They seemed to have presupposed some kind of mystical identity existing between Adam and all mankind. St. Augustine amplified the theory that Adam's sin is transmitted from parents to offspring in each generation through the sexual act, which, by virtue of the lust which accompanies it, is inherently sinful. In the Augustinian form the doctrine was adopted by medieval Roman Catholicism and later by Orthodox Protestantism.

Pelagius opposed Augustine by teaching that sin originates in man's following the bad example of Adam and that it is continued in mankind by force of habit. He denied original sin and man's hereditary guilt. Physical death, in Adam's case or that of his descendants, is not the result of sin but is necessarily involved in nature. He further taught that spiritual death is not the inherited consequence of Adam's sin but comes to each individual will that misuses its power of free choice by choosing to sin. Through reason and free will all men have the power to avoid making this unrighteous choice. If he so chooses, in the exercise of his free and morally responsible will, man may grasp the eternal aid of divine grace which is bestowed according to man's merit. Pelagius' major concern was to preserve the principle of human moral freedom over against Augustine's doctrine of man's total moral disability. Medieval Roman Catholic theology combined certain aspects of Pelagianism with Augustinianism and developed a doctrine of man which distinguished between the natural and the supernatural aspects of human nature. This new doctrine then declared that the fall of Adam entailed the loss of original righteousness in so far as the supernatural gift of divine grace was concerned, but not the destruction, only the staining, of the natural endowment of man (particularly his rationality and therefore his freedom) by which he is distinguished from the beasts. The Protestant Reformers rejected this doctrine of the dual character of human nature, eliminated all traces of Pelagianism from their teaching, and returned to a strict Augustinianism. They were constrained to emphasize the radical sinfulness of man over against the sovereignty of God, believing that their doctrine of salvation through grace alone required such teaching.[13]

Much of modern Protestantism gradually rejected the doctrine of the origin of sin in Adam's fall and the hereditary depravity of man. Yet, the old concept of original sin continues to be important in directing attention to two fundamental aspects of the Christian life—the recognition of the universality of sin and the acknowledgment of man's dependence upon divine grace.

Let us return now to the Genesis story. After God's creative work was completed, He pronounced this verdict upon His creation: "Behold, it was very good." (Genesis 1:31). Adam then was given some instructions in the Garden: "But of the fruit of the tree which is in the midst of the garden . . . ye shall not eat of it." (Genesis 3:3).

Man is finite and is thus limited. He is not God. His freedom to obey or disobey the divine command is assumed. Man is afraid to trust God and accept limits. Adam's rebellion is a decisive act of repudiation, a trusting of self over against God. As the Old Testament revelation unfolds, Adam's sin is reenacted in the life of God's children. Consistently they resist God's sovereign will and set themselves in rebellion against God's admonitions. Even in the prophets, sin's dominant motif continues to be rebellion against God. The first characteristic of sin then is related to freedom and man's misuse of the divine gift. The source of sin is not in man's contingent existence, but in his will which leads him into pride in open hostility to and rebellion against God.

The second element in the biblical view of sin is man's enthronement of self. He negates God and then substitutes self as another god, as an object of worship. Dynamic psychology speaks of this as narcissism. This is a form of idolatry. Possibly the Genesis narrative tempts man to overstep his bounds, "For God doth know that in the day ye eat thereof,

then your eyes shall be opened, and ye shall be as gods. . . ."
(Genesis 3:5). Such biblical statements as the one just
quoted touch the heart of man's perplexity. By exalting the
self beyond the limits God has decreed, man hopes to resolve
the tension arising out of the ambiguity of his existence as
both a child of nature and a child of the spirit. He usurps
the divine prerogative and claims the right to order his own
life and to become the center of his own world.

Usually the "self-ordered" life does not quiet man's
anxieties and fears. The very nature of his existence demands
a principle, a goal, a direction around which he organizes
and directs his life. Thus, it is not a matter of whether he
will worship and serve God or gods but rather of which
one he will worship and serve. Today, we have many gods,
and our society is filled with various forms of idolatry. The
ease and enthusiasm with which we follow the false gods
emphasize again to us the biblical concept of the depravity
of man as referring to the consequences of a broken relationship rather than to a substantial defacement.

THE PROBLEM OF EVIL IN DYNAMIC PSYCHOLOGY

A central task of dynamic psychology is to formulate
a theory of man based on the direct observation and study
of human action and experience in relation to the physical
and social milieu. This has been attempted by many, with
varying degrees of success and acceptance.

Psychology must not only debunk false ethical judgments but can, beyond that, be the basis for building objective and valid norms of conduct. I decry psychology's present-
day emphasis on *adjustment* rather than *goodness* and am
convinced that problems of ethics cannot be omitted from the
study of personality. This is especially relevant today when
many look upon neurosis as a symptom of moral conflict,

although adjustment is by no means a symptom of moral achievement. A moral conflict certainly expresses itself not infrequently as a neurotic symptom, so the success of the therapeutic effort would depend on the understanding and solution of the person's moral problem.

The sensitivity existing today about particular domains for psychology and theology has some relevance, but at times it narrows down to a sibling problem where one sibling is irritated by the other's proximity. Both disciplines are concerned with man but not exclusively so, especially for theology.* Thus, like two coins lying partly over one another, an area is shared by both coins and at the same time each also has separate areas.

The divorcement of psychology from ethics is a recent occurrence. The great humanistic ethical thinkers of the past were philosophers and psychologists. They believed that the understanding of man's nature and the understanding of values and norms for his life were interdependent. Freud made an invaluable contribution to the progress of ethical thought by debunking irrational value judgments but he took a relativistic position with regard to values. Such a position had a negative effect not only upon the development of ethical theory but also upon the progress of psychology itself.

Through many years of prolific writing and lecturing, Erich Fromm has spoken passionately for freedom, justice, and love, and has made great claims for the power of the human spirit.[4,5,7] No member of the profession of psychology and psychiatry has worked more diligently to teach man the way to freedom without loneliness, reason without rationalism, self-love without selfishness, authority without repression, and religion without theology. He is singled out in this discussion because of the relevance of his writings to the problem of evil.

Fromm declares his belief that destructiveness and evil are not inherent in man but are the results either of eco-

* As a theologian once expressed it: Psychology is concerned with man and man, while theology is concerned with man and man and God and man.

nomic shortages or of bad social institutions and relationships. The core of his work is the conviction that our civilization relentlessly and systematically crushes and corrupts man's deepest needs and noblest powers. Society is then really the sick one. Thus Fromm's discussion of corruption and regeneration proceeds neither in the language of the Jewish-Christian tradition nor in the language of Freudianism, but in the language of social reform. His sorrow is for man chained, isolated, and suffering, but Fromm's optimism leads him to a vision of man freed, his wounds healed, and restored to strength.

Fromm's diagnosis of the modern condition is rooted in psychoanalytic thought, and his discussion is usually carried on in psychoanalytic language, but his therapy is designed more to cure society than to relieve individuals of their neurotic burdens. Man is the victim of vicious institutions and has been chained by an evil society. Thus, the focus of Fromm's research is the "pathology of civilized communities." Freud has been called the Moses who showed the people the way out of the Egypt of their own passions, while Fromm is referred to as the aspiring Joshua who would lead them into the promised land of the sane society.[18]

Fromm's major failure has been his neglect or lack of recognition of "the evil" in man, or the dark side of man's life. At this point I am not speaking theologically but psychologically. When man is free, he is free to do evil as well as good. Fromm seems to be telling us repeatedly that man's real freedom depends not upon mastering his own passions and humbling his own pride but upon the reform of society. This surely cannot be the whole truth.*

The basic question of moral philosophy is the question of the origin and nature of evil and suffering. The two main answers are naturalism and supernaturalism.[18]

The supernaturalist sees all creation as incomplete, groaning and struggling toward completion. Thus the im-

* Fromm's optimism has been tempered somewhat in his book *The Heart of Man*.[6]

perfections and corruptions are emphasized. Since man is part of nature, he shares its imperfections, but he strives for the realm of perfection beyond nature. Although he may never reach this realm, his life will be good only to the degree that he struggles. Supernaturalism is very pessimistic, for its premise of the imperfection of created being forces the conclusion that evil and suffering cannot be conquered in this life.

Naturalism holds that nature is itself complete and inferior to no supernatural realm. Since man is a part of nature, he is also in himself whole and complete. The naturalist speaks primarily in terms of pain and pleasure. Pleasure refers to the satisfaction of man's needs and pain is their frustration. Naturalism cannot speak of good and evil for these are terms of moral judgment. The naturalist admits no realm of being and meaning outside nature by which nature can be judged. Although he cannot logically claim the categories of good and evil, he brings them into his system first by introducing the notion of the unnatural and then goes on to identify good with natural and evil with unnatural. Pain now can be used synonymously with evil and interpreted as the result of unnatural transgressions of nature's laws. These transgressions develop not out of any evil inherent in man, but from man's ignorance of the laws of nature or from his misguided efforts to change these laws through social action.

Society is the great corrupter of man, according to most systems of naturalistic thought. Society must be organized on natural principles and man must understand nature's laws, for evil can flow from attempts to tamper with nature without understanding her laws. Thus, evil flows from ignorance and good flows from a life lived in a society fashioned after nature. The naturalistic social philosopher tells us then to overthrow false customs, break down artificial restraints, study nature's plan through reason, and model society after nature's plan. This injunction for the developing of the perfect society was central in the optimistic thought of the Eighteenth Century as well as in the more pessimistic Social

Darwinism of the Nineteenth. Both groups confidently thought perfection would follow directly upon the ordering of society on natural principles.

Naturalism's history shows two main tendencies, one optimistic and the other pessimistic.[18] The Social Darwinists, pessimistic in their view of nature, held that pain and suffering are in the constitution of nature. Thus, nothing man could do would alter the grim fact that only the fit survive through deadly struggle against the weak. The optimists such as F. M. Ashley Montagu argue that love and mutual aid are as much a part of nature's plan as the survival of the fittest. The difference in mood seems to stem either from the philosopher's view of nature or from his view of man. At this point Freud has set forth his profound pessimism. His emphasis that the taint was in man, himself, left little hope for measures of social amelioration. Pain is the price paid for civilization, for without imposed restraints man is only the most capable of the beasts of prey. In *Civilization and Its Discontents,* he gives us the chilling words that men are not gentle, friendly creatures wishing for love, who simply defend themselves if they are attacked, but that a powerful measure of desire for aggression has to be reckoned as part of their instinctual endowment.[3] He amplified this further by saying that their neighbor is to them not only a possible helper or sexual object, but also a temptation to them to gratify their aggressiveness on him, to exploit his capacity for work without recompense, to use him sexually without his consent, to seize his possessions, to humiliate him, to cause him pain, and to torture and kill him.

In summary, naturalism as a philosophy declares nature as complete in itself and inferior to no other realm. Since man is immersed in nature, he is subject to all its laws. Also naturalism is a theory of morals based upon the concept that what is natural is good and what is unnatural is evil. This distinction between natural and unnatural is introduced to bridge the gap between pleasure and pain (descriptions of physical states) and good and evil (descriptions of moral states).

The chief difference between naturalism and supernaturalism as regarding the problem of good and evil seems clear. The naturalist holds that evil flows from attempts to stifle or violate nature through man's ignorance of nature's laws and his translation of that ignorance into social institutions. Thus, the dialectic of the human life is the struggle between man's desire to follow nature and man's tendency to violate nature and to suppress or corrupt his own natural needs. From the standpoint of the supernaturalist, nature itself is imperfect, and evil is inherent in its constitution. The creative dialectic then is man's struggle to overcome the imperfections of the City of Man and climb toward the perfections of the City of God.

The humanist puts man at the center, in a realm uniquely his own and resists any effort to pull man down into nature's realm or see him humiliated before a transcendental power.

It seems that Fromm's humanism is really naturalism in disguise and which manifests itself most clearly in his conception of good and evil.[18] As has already been stressed, naturalism regards goodness as inherent in nature and evil as the result of deviations from nature. Thus, evil is the frustration of natural needs and good is the gratification of these needs. Usually society is the one responsible for frustrating these needs. One discovers readily in Fromm's writings his basic point that man himself does not in any real sense make the criterion for virtue and evil but only *discovers* it in his own nature and the laws which govern its growth.

Fromm departs from the naturalistic thesis by contending that man is qualitatively different from the other animals, for he has psychological needs peculiar to himself and shared by none of the other creatures. Thus, where the earlier naturalists insisted that Utopia would arrive when man's physical needs were met, Fromm emphasizes certain psychic needs which must be satisfied if man is to achieve a fully human life.

Fromm's theory does not seem logical in a crucial area. He speaks of the reality of evil and assumes a tension between evil and perfection. It seems inconsistent to hold both that evil is real and that nature, including human nature, is without it. According to Fromm's position, nature is complete in itself and inferior to no other realm, and everything that exists in nature is natural. Since Fromm asserts that evil exists, is he not saying also that evil is natural? Thus, one reaches the absurd position where he is saying that what is natural is good, it follows that evil is good. This then brings us to the ancient wisdom that a moral theory which admits the existence of evil can locate the standard of perfect good only outside nature.

No individual in the field of psychology has emphasized the importance of an awareness of evil as has Carl Jung. He holds a strongly opposing view to that of Fromm. He speaks of evil in man as a "shadow," and groups under this term much of the primitive and instinctual in the psyche. He emphasizes that everyone carries a shadow, and the less it is embodied in the individual's conscious life, the blacker and denser it is. Discussions regarding the nature of the shadow, the recognition and acceptance of it, run as a central theme through the writings of Carl Jung. He writes that the shadow-side of man's nature is not just made up of small weaknesses and blemishes, but possesses a positively demoniac impetus.

Unfortunately man refuses to recognize the dark side of human nature. He struggles blindly against the dogma of original sin, which Jung declares is nevertheless utterly true.[12]

Jung states that in exploring the unconscious, the individual is confronted with the abysmal contradictions of human nature, and this confrontation in turn leads to the possibility of a direct experience of light and darkness, of Christ and the devil. Jung contends that without the recognition and experience of the opposites there is no experience of wholeness and hence no inner approach to the sacred. Thus, Christianity rightly insists on sinfulness and original sin, with the obvious intent of opening up the abyss of universal opposition in every individual.

Something of a summary statement of his concept of evil is given by Jung in the introductory chapter of *Psychology and Alchemy*.[11] He states that during the process of treatment the dialectical discussion leads logically to a meeting between the patient and his shadow. Jung speaks of the shadow as that dark half of the psyche which we invariably get rid of by means of projection—either by burdening our neighbors with all the faults which we obviously have ourselves, or by casting our sins upon a divine mediator. He goes on to say that without sin there is no repentance and without repentance, no redeeming grace; and that without original sin, the redemption of the world would never have come about. Evil needs to be pondered just as much as good, according to Jung, for good and evil are ultimately nothing but ideal extensions and abstractions of doing, and both belong to the chiaroscuro of life. He contends that in the last resort there is no good that cannot produce evil and no evil that cannot produce good.

Thus, the shadow symbolizes one's "other aspect," one's "dark brother," who, although invisible, yet belongs inseparably to the totality of the human personality. This dark aspect represents what an individual rejects in his nature and keeps in suppression because it stands in contradiction to his conscious principles. Conditioned by the mechanism of projection, this dark aspect appears as "the other one is always guilty," when one refuses to recognize that the darkness is in himself. Jung spoke of how the shadow as an archetypal figure often appears personified in many forms in the conceptions of primitives. It means sorcery to the primitive when someone treads upon his shadow, and its evil effects can be made good again only by a series of magical ceremonies.

The shadow also is a popular and frequently treated theme in art, for the artist's inspiration and choice of themes come from the depths of his unconscious. The figures of the unconscious rise in him and appeal powerfully to him, although he may not know where their fascination comes from. Examples of the artistic use of the shadow motive are Shakespeare's Caliban, R. L. Stevenson's Mr. Hyde, Mary G. Shelley's *Frankenstein*, Oscar Wilde's story, *The Fisher*

THE DARK SIDE OF MAN

and His Soul, Adelbert Von Chamisso's *Peter Schlemihl,* Hermann Hesse's *Steppenwolf,* Hugo Von Hofmannsthal's *Frau ohne Shatten* and Joseph Conrad's Kurtz, Gentleman Brown, and Leggatt. Although strictly speaking, the psyche is not a closed system, the hypothesis regarding the shadow and totality allows us to differentiate two sides of the personality, each side of which shows behavior, which is more or less complementary to the other side.*

Long before Jung dealt with this subject, Nietzsche showed that the concept of good always implies the concept of evil, and that not only love and hate, but also the *yea* and the *nay* belong together—that is, are complementary to one another. In Nietzsche's *The Wanderer and His Shadow,* the shadow is an earthbound figure who pursues the smallest and most immediate things of daily life and complements the eccentric figure of the lonely wanderer on the celestial heights.

In mythology one sees first of all the unequal brother-pair, which clarifies the relationship between the *one* and the *other.* In such myths the shadow appears as the "dark brother," who not only accompanies his light counterpart everywhere, but who also intrudes in a disturbing way, causing conflicts. Cain killed Abel who was the "light brother" favored by God, and Jacob cheated Esau, the "dark brother," out of the rights of the first born. It should be remembered, however, that in Jungian psychology, the shadow is not only something negative in the development of man, but as in the Gilgamesh epic it can be of great value for the individual. Not only past experiences, emotions, feelings, and instincts attach themselves deep in the unconscious to the shadow, but also the superior, the universally human, and creative can be sensed there.

Thus, when a person remains connected with his

* A study was once done of the dreams of the inmates of a federal penitentiary and the sisters of a convent. The prisoners, whose lives had been filled with aggressive and antisocial behavior dreamed of healing and helpful services rendered to mankind. The nuns, whose lives were filled with good deeds, dreamed of violence, rape, and all forms of instinctual behavior.

shadow, he reflects warmth and genuine humanity, for through his shadow the individual remains in contact with his natural, primitive side, and also with his body. Writers through the ages have spoken of how the shadow can be lost or actually how one could be born without a shadow and therefore lack truly human characteristics. Hugo Von Hofmannsthal in his *Woman Without a Shadow*[9] drew such a picture in the daughter of a supernatural king. Because of her lack of shadow she remained altogether excluded from the mystery of femininity, of pregnancy, and of birth. It is no accident, then, that the shadow is valued so highly among primitive people. Each considers it a treasure which he has to protect, for if one's shadow is injured, his actual life is also injured. The primitives also are afraid to touch the shadow of a powerful person, for this may bring death to them.

During the 1961 summer session at the C. G. Jung Institute in Zurich, I heard Barbara Hannah, a Jungian psychoanalyst, discuss Jung's concept of the shadow in the context of the biblical story of Jacob and Esau. She stated that Jung interpreted the angel who wrestled with Jacob as representing the family demon. Or one could be more direct and say that Esau was the angel, for actually he was the "dark one" in the family. Jung also emphasized that in the same way that man has a dark or shadow side, so has God. Therefore, the angel who wrestled with Jacob could be interpreted as a representative of the dark side of God. In such an interpretation, the positive side of evil is clearly illustrated in Jacob's statement to the angel, "I will not let thee go, except thou bless me." (Genesis 32:26).

Patients sometimes comment on how the Old Testament God frightens them. The contrast between the Old Testament and the New Testament God is usually explained as a matter of the progressive revelation of God. That is, in the beginning men were able to receive, accept, and understand only very feebly the revelation of God, and as He revealed Himself to them He was much more like they were themselves. As their own spirituality developed, and as they grew in spiritual dimension, their concept of God grew and they were ready for the higher form of God's revelation. Thus, as the centuries pass, man evolves through revelation a higher and higher concept of God, His principles, and His ethical requirements. This is demonstrated clearly as one moves from the early prophets into the New Testament era.

It seems relevant here to discuss Jung's belief about the necessity of having the feminine or earthly principle as a part of the godhead. Jung has always insisted that there should be a feminine aspect of God, and that the feminine should be a part of the Trinity. He feels that the Roman Catholic Church has solved this quite well through the Virgin Mary, but that Protestantism has not kept abreast of the times, and so it remains a man's religion which allows no metaphysical representation of woman. Jung feels that Protestantism has ignored the growing recognition of the equality of women and the vast importance of the feminine aspect of God and the goddesses that occupy a strong part of the myths and folklore of the past. Jung states that the proclamation of the new dogma of the Assumption of the Blessed Virgin Mary has a popular psychological need behind it. There has been a deep longing in the masses for an intercessor and mediatrix who would at last take her place with the Holy Trinity and be received as the Queen of Heaven and Bride at the Heavenly Court.[10] Thus through this dogma the feminine and earthly principle finds its place in the symbol.

In ancient folklore and mythology the feminine or the earth itself represents the instinctual and, in a sense, evil. Also, in the Jewish tradition there are speculations concerning a feminine element in the cosmic process of creation.* Therefore, the entrance of the Virgin Mary as a part of the Trinity would accomplish two purposes: bringing in

* In the teaching of the Zohar, a thirteenth century compendium of nonorthodox Jewish traditions, the world is the outcome of sex-life within the divinity. Woman on earth, "small in her exile but powerful," is represented as an "expression of the *Matrona*"—the feminine principle in the deity.

81

the feminine quality and permitting the evil or instinctual side of life to enter the godhead. Jung insisted that this would get rid of the old concept of dualism, for if God is recognized as having a dark side, then evil can be explained without recourse to a devil.

In relation to the feminine principle in psychology, as well as the dark and instinctual as a source of healing, it is appropriate to mention the Black Madonna in Our Lady of Hermits Church, Einsiedeln, Switzerland, and comment on it from the standpoint of analytic psychology. The Madonna is a beautiful, polished, ebony black. In the Black Madonna the dark side of man's nature finds expression. She relates him to earth, nature, and his instincts. As such, she hopes to compensate for the "too light Christian consciousness" which has cut man off from the deeper source of his healing, namely the unconscious. As healing often comes from the dark and instinctual side, the Black Madonna can represent well this aspect.

On visiting this beautiful Church in Einsiedeln one cannot help being overwhelmingly impressed with the masses of people worshiping in reverence and in expectation at the feet of this Black Madonna in the Gnadenkapelle. Its symbolism seems meaningful and its message clear on some level to those who worship there. The statue was completed in 1466. It is a late Gothic work of art, not quite four feet high, from Northern Switzerland or Southern Germany.[16]

RESOLVING THE CONFLICT AND FINDING A COMMON GROUND

In looking at man in his human quandary, both theology and dynamic psychology share the deep awareness of man's tragic alienation. This is poignantly illustrated for modern man by the ancient parable of the Prodigal Son (Luke 15:11–32). Although the church may formulate the truth of

82

this parable in dogmas or in sacraments of penance and absolution, it expresses also the condition of man as behavioral science sees him today. Man is in exile, impoverished, guilty over having wasted his substance, yearning for the home he abandoned in youthful rebellion, and not sure whether he can ever go home again.

Probably the artist, best of all, through the years has seen issues in perspective and teaches us how to bridge the gap of our differences. Thomas Wolfe is such a man and he portrays in words our condition: "Naked and alone we came into exile. In her dark womb we did not know our mother's face; from the prison of her flesh have we come into the unspeakable and the uncommunicable prison of this earth. Which of us has known his brother? Which of us has looked into his father's heart? Which of us has not remained forever prison bent? Which of us is not forever a stranger and alone?"[19]

Where can man find the answer to his alienation? Again both disciplines agree that he will find it in allegiance to God or some kind of god. It seems inevitable that man will make a choice. The biblical writer states it well: "I have set before thee this day life and good and death and evil; In that I command thee this day to love the Lord thy God, to walk in his ways, and to keep his commandments. . . . I call heaven and earth to record this day against you, that I have set before you life and death, blessing and cursing: therefore choose life that thou and thy seed may live." (Deuteronomy 30:15–19).

Thus neither the church nor dynamic psychology believes that man will find his alienation or emptiness an end within itself. Although many will not follow Kierkegaard's example and take a "leap into faith," they may at least understand psychiatrist-philosopher Karl Jaspers' dictum that only by passing through anxiety and hopelessness can the individual find a way to truth and faith. Jaspers himself follows a road between Kierkegaard and Nietzsche, "between revealed faith and atheism." His leap is the leap to transcendent thinking which brings him to reverence before transcendence. He attributes much of what is basic in his thinking to the Bible but has found some of the Christian doctrines confining and not liberating.

Fromm has echoed and reechoed the "human" qualities of man and declared that if man's "humanness" is allowed to evolve and express itself, we will have the sane society, characterized by human solidarity, love, and creative work. If Fromm is allowed to speak for one psychological group, we can select a churchman whose voice, in many areas, speaks a similar language—namely, Nicholas Berdyaev. Berdyaev, a Russian Orthodox Church thinker, had the unusual distinction of arrest and exile by both the Czarist and the Soviet governments. He voiced Dostoyevsky's passionate cry for freedom and the Eastern Church's ancient yearning that men should become divine. His central and persistent theme was the uniqueness and creativity of the self in defiance of the "thingification" of persons. He was critical of both communism and capitalism for their *use* of persons and urged a personalist socialism. For a quarter of a century, in his exile in Paris, he spoke compellingly to Christians and nonChristians everywhere. The existentialist Gabriel Marcel is also concerned with the way in which mass society, whether totalitarian or democratic, crushes personality. His answer is not the individualism of many existentialists. He starts with "we" rather than "I" and says that "we" do not know each other except as we live in the "mystery of being." He defines mystery as the core of the imaginative life. Personality, love, beauty, death, and Being are mysteries, and we live in wonder with them.

Another major area of agreement regarding the nature of man is his capacity and need for love and its relationship to normality. Freud was once asked what it was he would consider the ultimate in being normal. He replied: "*Arbeiten und lieben*—to work and to love." Thus normal and healthy in the psychological sense carries a connotation of human values, such as unremitting creative effort and love of one's neighbor.

The psychiatric movement has rediscovered the primary position of love in man's world. Much of what it stresses reaffirms and enriches the Christian idea of man. Thus in this emphasis on love, psychiatry and the Church find a mutual meeting place for hope as well as fruitful endeavor.

Both the psychological and the theological pictures of man share a profound pessimism over the nature of man, his bondage to evil, and his seeming inability to change. This comparison can be blurred by a too rigid interpretation of Calvin's concept of original sin or total depravity and by Freud's determinism.* C. Macfie Campbell put it this way: "Psychoanalysis is Calvinism in Bermuda shorts." Niebuhr has often attacked Fromm for what Niebuhr describes as an unrealistic optimism about human nature. Also, both theology and psychology have their followers who reject the pessimistic outlook regarding man.**

Theology speaks of the old and the new Adam and psychology of the infantile and the mature mind. Although these are not the same, there are similarities. Both suggest growth and change, commitment and renunciation. Both show the awareness of the past and of the future, the ability of man to look backward and forward, the recognition of an old self and a developing new self. Psychology as well as religion has its *Pilgrim's Progress*. Both accept man as always becoming.

Theology and psychology share a common understanding of man's tendency to equate knowledge with evil. Man's anxiety about his own search for knowledge and for power is reflected almost universally in myth and legend. For example, the

* Calvin stressed man's utter depravity and sinfulness. He emphasized the doctrine of original sin. Adam's sin had tainted the whole human race and robbed man of his goodness. Thus, because of this corruption, man was a child of evil. In some ways the original sin concept can be compared to Freud's concept of the id. Freud emphasized the strong biological and instinctual impulses of man as really being the controlling life force. Thus, there appears to be some similarity between Freud's concept of the id and Calvin's concept of original sin.

** A more optimistic outlook entered depth psychology with the introduction of Heinz Hartmann's ego psychology. In ego psychology the center of gravity shifts somewhat from the instinctual id to an autonomous ego, with emphasis on the autonomous, purposive character of human striving.

anxiety-producing qualities of atomic energy have been so great (apart from nuclear explosions in warfare) that the World Health Organization has been obliged to study this and issue a technical report on the *Mental Health Aspects of the Peaceful Uses of Atomic Energy*.[14] Many have commented on the magnitude of atomic power, its aura of mystery and magic, its imperceptibility, its almost infinite resource for good or evil, and the fact that while it affects everyone, the *control* rests in the hands of relatively few people.

The very young child first experiencing the world can be compared to the situation of man in relation to atomic power. There exists universally the feeling that man is punished for presumption. An example is Prometheus who in stealing fire, the prerogative of the gods, not only came to understand this prerogative but appropriated it for the use of men, and for this act of presumption was terribly punished. Pandora wantonly unleashed forces she could not control, because she also tampered with the prerogative of the gods. Since her action was accidental and innocent, mankind was left with *Hope*. The reverse was the situation with Faust, for when he evoked the Devil in order to assume the powers of God, there was nothing accidental about his action, and he was in consequence doomed to devastating punishment.

These represent some of the age-old attitudes of man in the search for *power*. There may be some attitudes of morbid satisfaction prevailing even today among people who predict and look for a kind of cosmic revenge on mankind. The association of knowledge with evil exists nowhere more explicitly than in the story of the experience of Adam and Eve in the Garden of Eden. A similar association is found elsewhere as in sayings such as this ancient Egyptian one: "When man learns what moves the stars, the Sphinx will laugh and life will be destroyed."

The universality of the feeling of man's punishment for presumption finds an arresting parallel in that universal experience of all men—being a child. The child is born helpless and completely dependent on powers which to him seem infinite, all-providing, but unpredictable—the source of almost infinite benefits or of ultimate destruction. Clinical evidence shows that children who come into conflict with parental power are prone to have phantasies of the most destructive type possible for them (including self-destruction). Also every child develops a capacity for aggressive action. Each child, though, in developing this natural aggressiveness must somehow gain control of it, if he is not going to be destroyed by it. If he does not, his blind aggression will make life impossible for him. The process of gaining satisfactory control is long, arduous, and subject to many failures. The greater the degree of control achieved by the child, the greater is his confidence and feeling of security. *It is the forces that appear uncontrollable that cause the deepest anxiety.* Thus both psychology and theology are confronted with this universal attitude of the human race as shown in mythology and the universal individual experience of childhood. Both also know the consequence of the individual's presumption in overextending himself, in declaring himself a god, and the anxiety associated with such action.

Both theology and dynamic psychology testify by the very nature of their work that man can and does change. Each is dedicated toward increasing man's capacity to solve his problems and to tap his latent resources. Both agree that man cannot be excluded from participating in the discovery and actualization of his own beatitude; that life can be ordered to good ends which enrich and fulfill personal and communal life. They share a common belief that love and truth generate an atmosphere in which human character matures and is transformed.

Both psychology and theology are meeting today on the platform of existentialism earnestly to seek answers to man's most ancient and yet most current problems: his cry for redemption, the overcoming of his separateness, the conflict between the counterfeit and the genuine self, and the shadow side of man's life.

At this point, however, I confess that the hospital and clinic have furnished me the most revealing setting for understanding sin and the operation of the moral order. In the consulting room, the drama of life unfolds in stark reality. The abuse of one's body or one's sense of values results in physical and emotional illness. When one challenges and violates the principles of his own value system or the laws of the universe, he does not succeed in breaking these laws. He breaks himself against them.

Only a moment's reflection will bring to mind many patients who offer grim testimony to this point of view. First there is the patient whose physician called a pastor and said, "I have been treating this patient for a stomach condition and have done all I can for him. His problem is really outside of the field of medicine. He has cheated his sister out of her inheritance. When he comes to grips with this and reaches a proper solution, he will no longer have stomach trouble."

I saw a beautiful red-haired girl in the hospital with a bleeding peptic ulcer. It became active and bled each time she became unfaithful to her husband and ran around with other men. The ulcer healed when she found forgiveness for the behavior which violated her interpretation of right and wrong.

Then there was the teen-age girl, wasting away in her hospital bed, vomiting and with no appetite. Her anorexia nervosa began after she had sexual intercourse for the first time with her boy friend. She could not bear the thought of having lost her purity, her innocence, and seemingly everything. Her wasting away was her atonement. Also the vomiting could have been an unconscious effort to rid herself of a fantasied pregnancy. She became well only when she solved her moral problem.

Thus the dark side of our lives cannot be projected on others but must be accepted, understood and worked with as it involves ourselves and our relationships with others.

REFERENCES

1. Barker, W. J. The western story. In Slovenko, R., and Knight, J. A., eds. Motivations in Play, Games and Sports. Springfield, Ill., Charles C. Thomas, 1967.

2. Conrad, J. Heart of Darkness and The Secret Sharer. New York, The New American Library, 1950.
3. Freud, S. Civilization and Its Discontents. (Trans. by Joan Riviere.) New York, Jonathan Cape and Harrison Smith, 1930, pp. 85–86.
4. Fromm, E. Escape from Freedom. New York, Rinehart, 1941.
5. Fromm, E. Man for Himself. New York, Rinehart, 1947.
6. Fromm, E. The Heart of Man. New York, Harper and Row, 1964.
7. Fromm, E. The Sane Society. New York, Rinehart, 1955.
8. Hick, J. Evil and the God of Love. New York, Harper and Row, 1966.
9. Hofmannsthal, H. Von: Frau ohne Shatten. New York, Boosey, 1943.
10. Jung, C. G. Answer to Job. (Trans. by R. F. C. Hull.) New York, Meridian Books, 1960, pp. 187–200.
11. Jung, C. G., Psychology and Alchemy. (Trans. by R. F. C. Hull.) New York, Pantheon Books, 1953, pp. 3–37.
12. Jung, C. G. The Psychology of the Unconscious. Collected Works of C. G. Jung. (Trans. by R. F. C. Hull.) London, Routledge and Kegan Paul, vol. 7, p. 54.
13. McCord, J. I. Know Thyself: The Biblical doctrine of human depravity. In the Nature of Man in Theological and Psychological Perspective, edited by Doniger, Simon. New York, Harper and Brothers, 1962, pp. 22–34.
14. Mental Health Aspects of the Peaceful Uses of Atomic Energy (WHO Technical Report Series No. 151, Geneva, 1958.)
15. Nietzsche, F. The Philosophy of Nietzsche. New York, Random House, 1927.
16. Raeber, Dom L. Our Lady of Hermits. Einsiedeln, Switzerland, Binzinger and Co., 1961, p. 20.
17. Sandrow, E. T.: Conscience and guilt: A Jewish view. In Noveck, Simon, ed. Judaism and Psychiatry. New York, Basic Books, 1956, pp. 24–31.
18. Schaar, J. H. Escape from Authority, the Perspectives of Erich Fromm. New York, Basic Books, 1961.
19. Wolfe, T. The Face of a Nation. New York, Charles Scribner's, 1939.

5

The Many Faces of Guilt

A physician acquaintance discussed with me a fifty-year-old patient he had seen in his home country of Colombia. The patient's hands were deformed in that the fingers turned inward toward the palms, resulting in what is described in medicine as "claw-hammer" type hands. When this patient was ten years old his uncle beat him fiercely. Later that day he passed his uncle's home and seeing no one there, he entered the porch. Beside the front door was the image of a man, made out of wood, and placed there to guard the house. This was the custom in that section of the country, and the wooden model was the image of the owner himself. The boy aimed his pointed canoe paddle at the heart of the model of his uncle and stabbed it. The model shattered to bits. Within hours he had lost the use of his arms. An aunt told him she could restore strength to his arms but that she could not save his hands. She worked for weeks and he did regain the use of his arms, but his hands remained in the claw-hammer position. Forty years had passed without change. His deformity had served as perennial punishment for his expression of violence and rage, had served always to neutralize his guilt for symbolically killing his uncle, and had furnished him great secondary gain from neighbors who out of compassion did many things for him.

Such a story raises many fundamental questions about the nature of guilt and its consequences, as well as its resolution.

DEFINITIONS OF GUILT

Professional groups often find themselves bewilderingly at cross purposes when they define and discuss guilt. In general, guilt is broken down into two types, although a multitude of terms such as the following ones are used: real guilt and guilt-sense; theological guilt and psychological guilt; real guilt and guilt feelings; being guilty and feeling guilty; real guilt and neurotic guilt; existential guilt and neurotic guilt. Possibly, a clearer grouping would encompass not two but three areas: (1) real guilt, (2) neurotic guilt, and (3) existential guilt.

Real guilt follows in the wake of wrongdoing, seen and accepted as such by the doer. He seeks expiation and makes restitution. It is a conscious phenomenon, involving deeds we have done.

Neurotic or pathological guilt has its roots deep in the unconscious mind, and the individual cannot rid himself of this by usual methods of atonement. In pathological guilt the intent, even unconscious, is equated with the deed, and the person reacts to the unconscious intent as if it were an already accomplished misdeed. Often the neurotic person of the obsessive-compulsive type unconsciously considers wrong what he unconsciously wishes to do. Thus, his endless rituals and gyrations to atone are understandable. They are endless because relief seems never to come. The depressed person may be dealing also with unconscious wishes, which he feels he has already carried out.

91

Existential guilt has some specific characteristics which must be understood, or else one is almost certain to confuse it with normal and neurotic guilt. First, everyone participates in it, for it is innate and a part of the very structure of being human. It is related to our failure to live up to our potentialities, as well as our failure in interpersonal relationships. No one reaches the goals he has set or should have set for himself. Also, who can say that his interpersonal relationships have been and are what they should be. Often they are disrupted with failures in communication or tendencies to use others for one's own sake.

Second, existential guilt does not come from cultural prohibitions or the taking unto oneself the values of one's parents but is rooted in the fact of self-awareness. It accompanies that ability of man to stand off and look at himself at a distance, to reflect upon himself. It is guilt that does not consist of violations of parental prohibitions, but arises from the fact that one can see himself as the one who can choose or fail to choose. Although its content may vary a little from culture to culture, every developed human being is confronted by this existential guilt.

Third, existential guilt is distinctly different from pathological or neurotic guilt. If unaccepted or repressed it may grow into or feed neurotic guilt. Many existentialists feel that in the same way that neurotic anxiety is the end-product of unfaced existential anxiety, neurotic guilt is the result of unconfronted existential guilt.

Fourth, existential guilt usually does not lead to the formation of symptoms but has constructive effects in the personality. It can lead to sharpened sensitivity in relationships with one's fellow man and increased creativity in the use of one's own potentialities.

The psychiatrist may extend further the meaning of guilt by speaking of a sense of guilt or consciousness of guilt which is so described "in disregard of the fact that the patient does not feel it and is not aware of it."[2] A sense which is not felt, a consciousness which is not conscious, may seem paradoxical, or even contradictory, but Freud's words express the finding that psychological analysis often shows that the need to be ill, the whole neurotic structure, is a disguise or substitute for a sense of wrongdoing which the patient is unable or unwilling to acknowledge. Also a profound and unconscious sense of guilt may manifest itself in one's consciousness and behavior as its very opposite, such as an aggressive self-righteousness, a projection upon others in constant fault-finding and moral censoriousness. Neurotic guilt may show itself not only in self-punishing and self-reproachful depression but also in a manic type of aggressiveness. This is not difficult to accept when one understands how easily a person projects onto others some of the contents of his own unconscious mind.

Also seen in the psychotherapist's consulting room is a guilt-sense which is actually a form of narcissism: an emotion-toned moral idealism, usually internalized from parents and teachers, which is largely unconscious and which makes failure to live up to its demands intolerable. This same phenomenon is a common factor in what the Roman Catholic Church describes as scrupulosity. The experienced confessor knows that the obsession of the scrupulous with their peccadilloes often proves to be an unconscious screen for a guiltiness of a much more rational and realistic character. A priest once remarked, "It is not their supposed vices but their supposed virtues which really stink." The Roman Catholic Church in dealing vigorously with the problem of scrupulosity has faced very clearly the problem of the difference between feeling guilty and being guilty, or neurotic guilt and real guilt.

The problem of understanding is further compounded when one hears the term "borrowed guilt feelings." "Borrowed guilt feelings" is a term used by Freud when the child internalizes the images of anxious, guilty parents. The subject may then feel guilty of sins that are not his own but which he has taken over or "borrowed" from someone else. Children have the habit of taking over the faults of their parents or others in authority. They are faults of which the child has been powerless to accuse his parents openly, or against which he is defenseless. He behaves as if he himself had committed

93

the sins and like a guilty person himself, or by committing other reprehensible acts to rid himself of responsibilities which are not his. .

Not infrequently the crimes of juvenile delinquents and adult criminals derive from feelings of guilt which were actually borrowed and incorporated long ago into the unconscious mind. Such an individual commits a crime because he is unconsciously seeking punishment as relief from his guilt-laden unconscious desires. However, not all such unconscious guilt is borrowed. Much of it may grow out of unconscious forbidden desires unrelated to the faults of others, and criminal acts may be committed to obtain relief-giving punishment.

O. Hobart Mowrer, Research Professor of Psychology at the University of Illinois, has written extensively on the subject of guilt. He decries the emphasis on "illusory" or "imaginary" guilt. He seeks to show that in psychopathology guilt is real rather than illusory.[4,5] He seems to be unaware of any present-day recognition and understanding of real guilt on the part of secular psychotherapists and assumes that they recognize all guilt as neurotic guilt. He feels that the psychotherapist encourages insight through the technique of free association when he should be working for repentance and restitution on the part of the patient. He declares that the neurotic's guilt is a state of sin and social alienation and that therapy must go beyond counseling to self-disclosure not just to the therapist but to the "significant others" in one's life. The process must then go on to active redemption in the sense of the patient making every effort within his power to undo the evil for which he has previously been responsible. This is necessary because the so-called neurotic is a *bona fide* sinner, that his guilt is from the past and real, and that his difficulties arise not from inhibitions but from actions which are clearly proscribed, socially and morally, and which have been kept carefully concealed, unconfessed and unredeemed.

Mowrer goes on to say that today those persons who are most deeply burdened and broken by personal guilt and moral failure are now quite regularly turned over by the churches to the state for care and treatment in mental hospitals. His statement involves the assumption that in so-called mental illness or psychopathology the central problem is guilt, unconfessed and unatoned real guilt. He feels that the state mental hospital as a therapeutic agency is a failure and that the time is upon us for rethinking the whole attempt to help guilt-ridden persons in a secular, medically controlled setting. The state has also been unsuccessful, according to Mowrer, in the treatment and rehabilitation of the legally guilty inmate of prisons. It appears, then, that secular, state-directed efforts to rehabilitate guilty people—both those who have been legally adjudged guilty (i.e., criminals) and those who are self-condemned (i.e., the insane)—leave much to be desired. In all fairness to Mowrer, it should be emphasized that his disappointment regarding rehabilitation is shared by many.

Usually theologians today share with psychiatrists the emphasis on a distinction between real guilt and neurotic guilt feelings. The theologian must be able to distinguish between the remorse which often passes for repentance but which does not issue in real forgiveness and reconciliation, and contrition which does.[6] Otherwise he may be puzzled by the man who writhes in a veritable torment of self-reproach and still finds no peace or else gains a false one. There is a definite distinction between normal and neurotic guilt, and we need to recognize this distinction if we are to understand human behavior.

Mention should be made of how guilt differs from shame. Guilt is generated whenever a boundary, set by the conscience, is touched or transgressed; shame occurs when a goal is not being reached.[7] Thus, shame indicates a real shortcoming and is related to failure, while guilt accompanies transgression. In the wake of guilt the individual fears punishment, but with shame he fears abandonment or contempt. Actually, a sharp distinction between shame and guilt should not be drawn, for the two overlap.

Anthropologists distinguish between shame and guilt cultures.[3] A shame culture is one which relies principally on shame as an external sanction for assuring conformity to the cultural norms. The reliance on a sense of guilt or conscience as an internal sanction for controlling behavior would be described as a guilt culture. In distinguishing shame and guilt cultures, shame is not the only form of external sanction or guilt the only form of internal sanction, but shame and guilt are the principal representatives of external and internal sanctions, respectively.

PHYSICAL ILLNESS AND GUILT

Guilt is related to physical illness in a variety of ways. At the outset, it should be said that physical illness is not always easily separated from the psychological, for the old categories of organic and functional have lost much of their separate meanings. However, for purposes of clarification in the organization of this material, I have chosen to break down the grouping of illness into physical and psychological.

It is generally conceded that hypochondriacal symptoms represent a form of self-punishment arising from guilt. These symptoms usually take the form of unpleasant bodily sensations such as itch, pulling, fullness or pain, bloating or anorexia. Characteristically, hypochondriacal symptoms have an insistent, demanding, nagging, and even persecuting quality which constitutes a source of great distress to the patient, who pleads for relief. These symptoms involve especially the skin, nose, abdomen, rectum, and genitalia. Associated with hypochondriasis, not infrequently, is the persistent idea of the presence of an organic disease. Although the adult is the one usually affected in this particular somatic way by psychological stress, the teenager is not immune. Teenagers often fear the presence of an organic disease such as syphilis, cancer, tuberculosis, or heart disease. The idea of a disease may also include symptoms related to the disease in question. The teenager has to cope with a multitude of feelings and situations with which he has had no previous experience. The increased sexual urges which sweep over him, his independent strivings which throw him in aggressive conflict with parents and other authority figures, plus his hostility toward his younger siblings, all combine to haunt him with a sense of guilt and loss of self-esteem. Thus, in his sleep he is bothered by nightmares and bad dreams, while during the day the fear of serious illness creeps into his mind. Some teenagers unfortunately solve the problem by suicide, the third leading cause of death among this age group.

Conscience plays a major role in hypochondriacal symptoms. Involved in a hypochondriacal system are deprecation, guilt, unworthiness, and usually satisfaction in self-punishment. Such patients have a strong sense of right and wrong and may seek punishment in handling their guilt. A frequent unconscious mechanism in them is an attempt to provoke the doctor to punish them. The more painful the treatment regimen, the better the therapy works for these patients.

The excessive use of pain as a psychological means of adjustment should be evaluated from the standpoint of guilt. Clinically, one finds either a long background of guilt and/or an immediate guilt-provoking situation. The clinical features of the chronically guilt-ridden person are not difficult to identify, if one understands the role of penitence, atonement, self-denial, and self-deprecation as means of self-inflicted punishment to ease the feeling of guilt. The guilty, self-deprecating attitudes are readily apparent in these individuals who are usually gloomy, pessimistic, and chronically depressed. Such people have usually suffered a large number and variety of defeats, humiliations, and illnesses. Many of these circumstances have either been solicited by the patients or simply were not avoided. These individuals drift into situations and submit to relationships in which they are hurt, defeated, or humiliated and seem not to learn from experience. No sooner are they out of one difficulty than they are in another in spite of obvious and strong warnings. Concurrently, they fail to exploit situations which should lead to success. If success is actually thrust upon them, they may do badly. Unconsciously, they feel that they deserve neither success nor happiness and that they must pay a price for even a token of good fortune. Many such patients are unusually tolerant of pain inflicted upon them by nature or by their physicians during physical examinations and treatment. Their medical histories are long and filled with an extraordinary number of injuries, operations, and painful illnesses. In the background of many of these patients, one often finds that aggression, suffering, and pain played a significant role in early family relationships. Some of the childhood experiences common to these persons which contribute to their strong feeling of guilt and their tendency to use pain as a means of psychic regulation are: quarreling between parents, harsh punitive attitudes and actual physical punishment, painful illnesses, exposure to others suffering pain or to scenes of violence, and a lack of warmth in human relationships.

Thus, early in childhood, pain and punishment become linked, and the association is established that pain is inflicted when one is "bad." Not only does pain come to constitute evidence that one really is bad, thereby acquiring the capacity to provoke feelings of guilt, but it frequently becomes the important medium whereby guilt is expiated. Children and adults may solicit and welcome pain as though it assures expiation, forgiveness, and, hence, reunion with the loved one. Engel summarizes this phenomenon: "Indeed, there are some children for whom reconciliation with an angry, punitive parent constitutes the most intense and gratifying experience in their lives. For them, to be 'bad' and then to be punished may become a way of life. When pain serves in this manner to alleviate guilt and to reestablish a relationship, pleasure in a relative sense is again involved. To feel despised and abandoned is much worse than to suffer pain at the hands of the object who cares enough to punish, especially if the punishment also results in forgiveness and reconciliation."[1] In all of us, pain was involved in the development of early relationships with others. In infancy, pain provokes crying. This cry for relief was answered by a loving and comforting mother. Then in childhood when an injury is sustained, mother or father "kisses the pain away." Thus a pleasurable element is introduced, but it is not the pain that is pleasureable. It is the association of the relief of pain with the reunion with a love object that is enjoyed. Thus there is embedded in the psyche of such individuals the slogan, "the pain is worth the price."

There are multiple facets to this complicated problem. "Why did this happen to me?" is a question the physician and clergyman hear daily. This is a common psychological reaction to physical illness. It is expressive of a guilty feeling that one's moral lapses have somehow brought the illness about. Associated with this guilty feeling is a melancholy sense of personal unworthiness and lowered self-esteen that often affects the patient enough to hamper his recovery. Patients with cancer are expecially prone to explore why such an illness has befallen them. One can clinically observe guilty feelings in probably a majority of these patients. They often try to identify some kind of personal failure as having a relationship to the development of cancer in them.

The use of physical illness to punish oneself through delay in getting surgical or medical treatment is now attracting widespread concern on the part of the medical profession.[9,10] The fear of punishment as a psychological determinant of delay characterizes a number of these patients. This fear is to be distinguished from the realistic expectation of pain or distress in diagnosis and treatment. Delay in seeking treatment is defined as a procrastination extending beyond the length of time a rational person in society might be expected to hesitate before visting a physician for treatment. This group's expectation of pain or mutilation is far in excess of the degree appropriate to the actual stress. Clinical psychiatric interviews and projective psychological tests reveal in the make-up of these patients a deep-seated guilt feeling in conflict with unacceptable hostile impulses toward significant persons in their environment. They have been conditioned by early experiences to expect retribution for such hostile impulses, and when afflicted with a surgical illness, they come unconsciously to believe that the day of judgment will arrive when they are strapped to the operating table in the surgical amphitheater. The fear of punishment manifests itself in markedly enhanced tension about the pain to be experienced or the mutilation to be imposed by the surgical procedure. Also they have unnecessarily gruesome fantasies about the means and form of surgical treatment.

Other patients show an exaggerated fear of death as a cause of delay in seeking surgical treatment and this group can be considered an extension of the fear of punishment in which the hostile impulses are perceived by the individual to be more intense and murderous, thus deserving the ultimate retaliation. The risk of a surgical operation is exaggerated in fantasy and, thus, anxiety is greatly accentuated. Characteristic of this group is a superstitious but intelligent, obese and hypertensive fifty-year-old woman who has long expressed her dependent needs vicariously by caring for hordes of children of working mothers at ridiculously low fees and at great personal sacrifice. She has endured a prolonged, mutually hostile relationship in her marriage. She waited through three months of severe postmenopausal bleeding before submitting to a medical examination, which disclosed a large tumor of the uterus. The psychiatric studies indicated that she was expectant of retaliation in the operating room commensurate with her own unconscious death wishes for the husband she had long supported. Shortly after the surgical procedure was performed, she was found to have resumed her former self-sacrificing mode of living.

Many delaying patients are individuals suffering severe and deepening depression prior to the onset of their illness.

Some of these patients have suffered separation or severe emotional deprivation and are involved in unresolvable conflict over their bitter rage provoked by frustration and their growing guilt over the inner perception of such feelings. They display signs of melancholy, apathy, indifference, irritability, feelings of worthlessness, and a pessimistic view of the future. When an illness requiring surgical intervention makes itself known, they resign themselves to passive suicide and death.

The other side of the coin must be considered also. The physician frequently sees patients who seek operations as a form of punishment for deep, underlying feelings of guilt.

THE MANY FACES OF GUILT

This is especially common in the borderline schizophrenic patient designated in psychiatric nomenclature as the chronic undifferentiated or ambulatory schizophrenic. When working in the emergency and admitting rooms of municipal hospitals, one sees such patients with multiple abdominal scars resulting from surgical procedures. Such patients may complain constantly of abdominal pain, and the surgeon finally operates, although none of the signs and symptoms are classic of a specific surgical illness. The first operation cures nothing. The patient returns frequently and often displays symptoms which are suggestive of adhesions from the previous procedure. Since such adhesions may cause intestinal obstruction and other serious complications, the surgeon is often led to operate again. Then there begins a continuous process which seems never to end and which gives such patients a medical file as thick as a large city's telephone directory. The pattern in certain severe neurotics is similar to the borderline schizophrenic. It all adds up to guilt and the seeking of punishment to relieve this guilt.

EMOTIONAL ILLNESS AND GUILT

Guilt as a product of the overly strict conscience plays a major role in symptom formation. As the mental agency concerned with right and wrong, goals and ideals, the conscience has a highly significant part in determining the form that illness might take. Functions of the conscience may be so exacting, harsh, and punitive that the patient not only suffers from inordinate feelings of guilt but may also excessively utilize techniques of self-punishment and atonement to alleviate or avoid feelings of guilt. A variety of emotional illness patterns may result in which the struggle with guilt feelings is predominant.

One major reaction of this type is depression characterized by intense feelings of self-abasement, self-deprecation, guilt, worthlessness, and a strong need to be punished, sometimes carried out by injury to self or suicide. A former assistant district attorney clearly fits this pattern.

This 58-year-old man sought psychiatric help because of feelings of tension and a deep depression. He had had similar spells characterized by the same symptoms since adolescence. He had always been overwhelmed with feelings of guilt and remorse, especially in his younger years. He knew this was foolish, for in all his life he had hardly committed "a good, full-grown sin." At his university during examinations he shielded his eyes and held his head down out of fear that he might see another's examination paper. In the margin of his examination papers he often wrote a confession that possibly he saw or heard a word which helped him. His professors never mentioned this, probably because he was one of the top students in his class. During a period when he clerked in a store, he worried when each customer left. "Did I give this person the right change or did I make an error in my favor?" After kissing a girl, especially what he described as deep kisses, he worried if he had given her some germ. In high school he won an oratorical contest. He decided afterwards that he had possibly received too much help and considered seriously for several weeks sending the medal he won to the student who placed second. He always had a tremendous need to confess everything, real or imagined, to someone.

He graduated in law and practiced for only three or four years. Law practice was too stressful for him. He suffered from numerous conflicts. While an assistant district attorney, he declined all cases in which the state asked for the death penalty. He generally won the court cases he accepted. He was a good speaker and had a flair for quoting poetry. He stated that the jurors frequently cried as he spoke, and at times he fell under the spell of his own words and wept also.

After quitting the practice of law, he began devoting considerable time to creative writing. He was the author of more than ten published books of fiction and verse and one play. Also, he contributed fiction and verse to many magazines and anthologies. His books had a good critical reception but very poor sales, due in part, according to the patient, to the fact that they were books of social protest—protesting against segregation, unfair labor practices, and so forth, long before these social issues became popular. His writings brought him only a very small income, but he found writing a very satisfying experience, although hard work. He felt that he made his contribution to the reforming of society through writing instead of active participation on committees or other community activity. His health would not permit him a more active participation, according to his assessment. He was frightened on the inside when he met people, and he felt he could not serve society well in any way except by writing.

The patient remembered nothing about his father, for his father died when the patient was only three years old. His mother died at the age of eighty. The patient was then forty-seven years old. He described her as a beautiful woman. She was very conscientious and reared all the children in a "strict, Methodist tradition." With the small income she inherited from her father's estate, she took care of the family's needs adequately and educated all the children. She was a nervous person and a true martyr. As a child the patient was very dependent on his mother. Even at age fourteen he could hardly leave his mother to go to camp. In his early teens he feared she would die, and often while she slept, he would steal into her room and listen quietly to see if she was still breathing. He disappointed her when he gave up his lucrative law practice and began his career of creative writing, for then he could not help her financially. He felt very guilty about this even at the time he sought treatment. Anyway, his tenderest and most admirable memories were about her, and he stated that if there were a heaven and he arrived there, he would seek her out and sing her a song of gratitude and praise.

Although he was reared a Methodist, he gave up this church affiliation after he became grown. His faith was then equivalent to Unitarianism. He had thrown aside consciously all strict religious beliefs but felt that these might well be grounded in his unconscious mind and bestir themselves frequently to torment him.

One can speculate on the basis of clinical data regarding the motivation underlying this patient's behavior. His father died when he was three, just at the stage of psychosocial development when a little boy would feel extremely close to his beautiful and overprotective mother. The mother was left with seven children to rear, with the modest estate her husband and father had left her. Most likely she felt much unconscious rejection of those children because of the great responsibility of caring for them after her husband's death. In the wake of unconscious rejection came guilt feelings, and to atone she became an overprotective mother, a martyr. She succeeded in keeping her children dependent and bound to her in such a way that the patient and all the other siblings except one have remained unmarried. The patient always had strong feelings toward his mother, growing out of the early oedipal ties from which he never freed himself. Also, there must have been tremendous anger toward his mother for this enslavement. He was caught in a double bind. He could not remain with her, yet could not get away to mature and become an independent, aggressive male who could and would assume his masculine role. He had some rebellious moments, such as when he gave up his law practice, which his mother was proud of, and turned toward creative writing. His anger was so frightening and distasteful to him that his whole life was guilt-ridden. His self-esteem was always very low, and for his imaginary transgressions, he punished himself long and persistently. Thus, depression was his constant companion. This depression was frequently incapacitating. He attained a measure of adaptive success through creative writing. What this writing meant to him, one can only speculate. He published numerous books and continued to write. It could possibly be postulated that the patient almost had an addiction for writing. Also, he may have pursued his creative endeavour to absolve himself of his destructive and hostile feelings. In other words, this was a kind of atonement which he offered up daily. He refused to compromise and rewrite or change certain parts of his manuscripts just to make his writings more marketable. A factor to consider was his possible need to fail as punishment for his sins. He was forever seeking forgiveness, and success and fame as a writer would be the opposite of punishment. Thus, here was a man in bondage to cyclic bouts of depression. His life had been a long story of self-punishment. Although in his own conscious thinking he had never committed what could be called "a big sin," one can assume that in his unconscious there were strong determinants of his behavior (classed there as big sins) of which he had only the shadow of an awareness.

Since depressive illness is so intimately tied to guilt and self-punishment, I am reviewing the widely accepted dynamic pattern in depressive illness.

No psychiatrist has been more articulate and clear in elucidating the dynamic pattern in depression than Sandor Rado.[8] He pictures the depressive spell as a desperate cry for love, precipitated by an actual or imagined loss which the patient feels endangers his emotional and material security. The patient has lost his loved one. The emotional over-reaction to this emergency unfolds, without the patient's awareness, as an expiatory process of self-punishment. Through blaming and punishing himself for the loss he has suffered, he hopes to reconcile "the mother" and to reinstate himself into her loving care. His dominant motivation of repentance, though, is complicated by the simultaneous presence of an intense resentment. His guilty fears push him toward humility and repentance; and his coercive rage pushes him toward resentfulness. In the forephase of the depressive spell, the patient has a tendency to pour out his resentment on the beloved person, the one who deserted him or let him down. This is an effort to force the person to love him. When the patient feels that his coercive rage is defeated, his need for repentance becomes dominant. His rage then recoils and turns inward against himself, increasing by its fervor the severity of his self-reproaches and self-punishment. As a supreme maneuver for forgiveness, the patient may even be driven to suicide. As he attempts to end his life, he seems to be acting under the illusion that this supreme sacrifice will reconcile the loved one and secure her nourishing graces forever.

In the simplest form, the depressive spell of the adult is related to the depressive spell of the infant. The person simply says, "I have no mother and no father. What have I done to cause me to lose them? I must seek some kind of forgiveness in order to get them back." Then the person begins to make proper restitution and atonement through various types of maneuvering for forgiveness.

Another reaction to the harsh and punitive conscience is that of the masochistic pattern. This is characterized by one or several of the following features: martyrdom; a predilection for painful, disagreeable, and defeating situations; a proneness to accidents, injury, or surgery; an intolerance of success and good fortune; and a tendency to sabotage oneself especially in his work or career.

A case representative of this category is that of a tall, handsome 39-year-old worker who sought psychotherapy because of tension headaches. His excellent command of language was impressive. Although his formal education extended only through high school, his store of knowledge was great. He had many interesting hobbies from organ building to collecting 19th century Springfield rifles. He was well informed in electronics and mathematics. The most impressive aspect of his life was that though he had great ability and a sizeable store of information, he was holding a mediocre job in an industrial plant—working in a tool room. His assigned duties were not a challenge and probably did not require even a small portion of his skills. A review of his history revealed that on several occasions in different settings he had worked himself up to a promotion of a fairly high level, and he would then invariably quit and seek another job. Frequently there were some realistic factors in his quitting and moving, and at other times the factors did not seem realistic. Thus, this is a story of a man who seems to sabotage himself at critical periods in his advancement.

What does it mean when one practices this type of self-sabotage? Intensive and deep probing is often necessary to uncover such dynamics. Some of the more common theories are: fear of success because of what it means—e.g., leaving your peer group through advancement and then running the risk of being rejected by fellow employees; fear of competition which always exists when one moves into a more favorable work status; fear of increased responsibility and the greater possibility of failure; an unconscious desire to fail as a form of punishment for some real or fantasied wrong committed in the past; fear of overcoming and advancing beyond the father (this may sound strange but it is fairly well documented by psychoanalysis that certain individuals seem to hold themselves back so as not to surpass or at times equal the father's accomplishments, although their potential is greater); deep feelings of inadequacy which come to the surface when a bigger job is offered—"this new job is a man's job and I am still a boy"; and a desire to fail as punishment of his family toward whom he is hostile, for they use him only as "a work horse."

It is usually helpful to point out some of the dynamic factors often seen in self-sabotage, without direct application to the person to whom one is talking, when only brief psychotherapy is available for the patient. This initiates a process of introspection, aided some by the brief psychotherapy, which not infrequently uncovers some of the specific dynamics related to the person's failure. In the patient described here I could identify vast quantities of guilt and rage in relationship to authority. He was treated psychotherapeutically in this area. Without any intervention on the part of anybody with his supervisors, he assessed his working environment, began applying himself in a more creative and intelligent way and in a matter of months earned for himself a major promotion to a job which challenged his ability and skills. As his work situation improved, his tension headaches diminished.

A third reaction to the harsh and punitive conscience is perversion masochism in which sexual pleasure is possible only at the expense of pain inflicted by the sex partner.

In such severe cases, the individual may recurrently

place himself in a hurtful role as a necessary condition for sexual gratifications. Sexual feelings cannot be experienced as exclusively pleasurable sensations and are always associated with "hurt" of some kind. The sexual act becomes an experience in which one hurts or is hurt. Thus, in order to fulfill the basic sexual needs, life becomes a series of humiliating experiences, associated with constant disruption of human relationships. Although individuals of this type enjoy the sexual act very little, they cannot give it up. To be rejected, humiliated, or hurt becomes the only avenue which leads to any sexual enjoyment.

The so-called "moral masochist" should not be confused with the "perversion masochist." The moral masochist continues his diversionary maneuvers as a defense against anxiety without ever achieving pleasure. Nothing will divert him from his goal. Since his goal is actually pleasure, he is convinced that one day he will actually achieve it, and the more he suffers, the sweeter will be his reward. At the other extreme of masochists (with the whole range of mixed types in between) is found the perversion masochist—one who achieves his goal and obtains pleasure, orgasm, behind the protection of the masochistic mechanism. In this category are placed all those who seem to buy pleasure by what is generally and erroneously considered to be self-punishment. Its fraudulent nature is demonstrated by the fact that often a purely symbolic act is sufficient. This is illustrated by the woman masochist who had an orgasm every time she knelt. The ways in which masochists behave to attain their desired aim vary from real pain on the one hand to a symbolic gesture on the other.

The literature as well as any psychotherapist's files abound with clinical material which attest to the strange and peculiar varieties of sexual behavior associated with masochism. There is the young woman who made her husband beat her during sexual intercourse and who came to the psychotherapist complaining of frigidity and extremely severe attacks of anxiety. Then there is the young man who every few weeks came to the city from his little town and visited a house of prostitution famous for its beautiful girls. He was a regular customer, so the madam always made the arrangements he requested. His requirements were always the same. All the girls in the house had to strip and assemble naked in a large room. He would come into the room naked also and run around the circle of girls. As he ran, they would beat him vigorously on the buttocks with leather belts. Similar activity was described by a prostitute who was seen in the outpatient psychiatric clinic of a municipal hospital. She reported that when she was new in the business of prostitution she was not as shocked by the sadistic men who inflicted pain on her as a part of the sex act but by those who required all kinds of punishment from her before they could or would perform and even during the sexual act. Polly Adler emphasizes this also in her book *A House Is Not a Home.*

Before leaving this subject it should be mentioned that it is difficult to separate masochism from sadism. This accounts for the widespread tendency today of using the terms together—sadomasochism. In a sadomasochistic relationship, there is no sharp line dividing the roles. Case histories of sadists and masochists constantly reveal traces of both groups of phenomena in the same individuals and suggest that the two are so closely related they can be regarded as representing the same perversion.

The fourth reaction to the exacting and punitive conscience is an obsessve-compulsive neurosis which is frequently called guilt neurosis. In this syndrome, guilt leads to exaggerated magical techniques of doing and undoing, isolation, and reaction formation as means of coping with forbidden impulses.

Case material to illustrate this kind of patient and the psychodynamics involved is taken from teaching files at Tulane School of Medicine.

A 39-year-old woman was admitted to the hospital with a presenting problem of severe disabling compulsions for fifteen years. The decompensating compulsive rituals began when the patient was nursing her mother-in-law. She first became preoccupied with obsessive death wishes toward her mother-in-law and overcompensated for these by exhausting herself physically in nursing her. She waited on the mother-in-law to the degree that she lost sleep, became physically run down, and developed a respiratory illness herself. It was shortly after her mother-in-law's death that the patient gave birth to her daughter. At this time the father-in-law asked her to assume the maternal role in his home. The patient, although overloaded with guilt over her mother-in-law's death, refused to do this. Her refusal was associated with overt expression of anger toward the father-in-law who shortly developed a sudden illness and died. Immediately following this, her overt ritualistic activity began.

On admission it was noted that the patient was an attractive, meticulously dressed, middle-aged woman who appeared in good health. She was extremely attentive and her manner was somewhat ingratiating. Her facial expression was one of anxiety, sadness, hopelessness, and fear. She was emotional and cried tearfully on several occasions. She appeared quite depressed when talking of the incapacitating nature of her compulsions.

The patient could not remember the exact date when her compulsions developed, but stated that the onset seemed to be associated with her pregnancy and the death of her parents-in-law fifteen years ago. The first symptoms were hand washing compulsions and a phobia of dirt, vomitus, feces, and bathroom odors. About three years ago she developed a compulsion to wipe herself clean with rags. Her fears and compulsive wiping had become progressively more bothersome. At the time of admission the patient was unable to do any of her housework. She had been avoiding the bathroom, her own kitchen, and her avoidance behavior had spread to involve vomitus, dead things, and Italian cheese (all because of odor). She had been using one rag for the lower part of her body, another one for the upper part, and another one for her face and arms. She had to stand in the corner of the kitchen to eat her meals. She had been unable to go shopping or sit in the movies because of fear of touching someone who had eaten Italian cheese or that the odor might envelop her.

THE MANY FACES OF GUILT

The patient found herself staying in her house for weeks at a time to avoid being contaminated. About three weeks prior to admission, the symptoms became markedly worse following the death of her neighbor's cat in her back yard. This produced depression and occasional suicidal thoughts. She had insight to the extent of realizing the symptoms were illogical and even called them absurd.

The patient was the elder of two children. Both parents were described as overly protective of the children. The patient was always particularly close to her mother, who was described as a meticulous, rigid and orderly person, always concerned first and foremost with the cleanliness and orderliness of her home. Both mother and patient described with pride that the patient was completely toilet trained at the age of six months. The patient was described as an exceptionally "good girl" throughout her life. The parents were devoutly religious and the patient has continued as a devout churchgoer. A principal source of pride in her early life was her meticulousness and orderliness. She stated that nothing was ever out of place. For example, in early adolescence she straightened her dresser drawers regularly even though they were not in need of it. Both patient and mother proudly reported that the patient always completed all of her homework immediately upon returning home from school before playing with other children or seeking other frivolous pleasures.

At the age of nineteen she married a man four years her senior. Shortly after marriage she became pregnant, and during this period her husband's parents became ill. From her description she played an overprotective role with her daughter, emphasizing with gestures that she managed to toilet train her daughter at the age of seven months. It was during the first year of her daughter's life that the patient's rituals became so severe that much of the responsibility for managing her home had to be turned over to her mother. During the ensuing fifteen years it has been apparent that it was the mother who bore the brunt of the patient's illness. The more decompensating her rituals became, the more responsibility her mother was forced to assume. The patient described her

111

daughter as being just like herself in that she is extremely orderly to the point of being ritualistic; that she considers her duties first and foremost and as taking precedence over the usual activities indulged in by other children. The daughter has suffered from chronic recurrent colitis.

A look at obsessive behavior and the underlying motivation involved seems indicated to understand better the patient presented.

The genesis of these behavioral trends in the obsessive neurotic patient becomes clearer as one learns of the ideal social milieu or early family environment found consistently in the obsessional patient. A necessary requisite is an obsessive mother. This type mother is a poor disciplinarian. Because of the symptoms related, she is overdemanding, meticulous, impatient, and intolerant. Her interest centers on unimportant issues, principally training, because of her inability to show warmth and love. With such a parental relationship, the child is driven into defiance as a result of overrestriction, attempts to revolt, and is punished by the unyielding obsessive mother. A terrific conflict results because the child, to be safe, wishes to remain in the good graces of the mother. The child's reward, in this environment devoid of love and affection, is only to gain service and respect from the parent. Because of the early interrelationships, the obsessive revolt is characteristic of the child prone to develop the obsessive neurosis. Inevitably, obsessive patients give histories of temper tantrums in childhood. These create tantrums in the obsessive mother in return and she, being stronger, smothers this mode of expression in the child. The outcome is a deadlock which sets the pattern of adaptation in the child, the outcome of which is an unending struggle between the two sustained and equally strong emotions of rage and fear.

Because of the nature of our society, much of this initial restriction of the child by the parent is in the area of habit or toilet training. This is particularly pronounced with an obsessive mother who is prone to place prime importance on control of bladder and bowels. This is apparent in the case just discussed. The patient demonstrated her maximum pleasurable response and was overwhelmed with pride when describing her success on having her child toilet trained at the age of seven months, and boasting that she had been toilet trained at the age of six months by her mother. From her description of the relationship with her child during that period, it is apparent that this bathroom-centered activity was the focal point of their relationship. In the child's mind, this activity loomed as the most important function of her life. It is little wonder that concentration on such socially insignificant factors in the area of behavior should persist in their importance. Such a mother creates the exaggerated idea in the child's mind that feces is poison, and this is readily elaborated into the concept that all dirt is poison. The intense emotionality centered about feces spreads to become associated with all bodily fluids. Thus, all bodily fluids become vehicles for expression of rageful feelings, and their avoidance becomes a means of gaining approval. The vagina, in propinquity to the anus, becomes similarly considered as a dirty hole or sewer. Thus, dirt, feces, poison, and all bodily fluids are items of intense concern. The antidote stressed by the mother is washing, cleanliness, orderliness, meticulousness, use of antiseptics, and so on. Such activity on the part of the child appeases the mother and lessens the threat of punishment for the child.

The fifth reaction to the harsh and punitive conscience is "psychogenic pain." This is the suffering of pain as an experience primarily psychological or secondarily solicited from the environment in the form of injuries or operations in which the pain serves to attenuate guilt and permit a small amount of success and gratification.

A 46-year-old woman whom I shall call Nan illustrates well how pain operated in an effort to attenuate guilt over sexual transgressions.

Early one Saturday morning, the man with whom the patient was living served her coffee and fruit juice in bed. This was not an unusual practice for him, when he had to go to work early. Later in the morning, she arose but noticed that she had no "pep" and felt a little depressed. She could think of no reason for feeling this way. Instead of preparing for herself some breakfast as she usually did, she decided to have a bottle of beer. She continued drinking until she had consumed eight or ten bottles. This was remarkable for her, because prior to this she never drank alone or consumed at one time more than one cocktail or bottle of beer.

Then without premeditation, she decided to shoot herself. She went to the dresser drawer where a pistol was kept, took it out, fired it twice into her right side, and fell across the bed with the pistol beside her. She stated, "This was a momentary impulse—something that can't be explained." She went on to say that after she shot herself she remembered thinking, "Now what have I done!" She was in such pain by now that the agony consumed all of her thinking.

An estimated two hours after the shooting, her "man" came home and discovered her. She vaguely remembers his coming in and finding her on the bed. He saw the blood and the pistol and was almost panic-stricken. He asked, "Honey, what did you do?" And then after pulling himself together a little, he said that he would have to call the police. She remembers seeing the police and the doctor enter her room. She can recall nothing else until much later when she awoke at the hospital as from a dream and was glad to find herself alive.

She arrived at the hospital in shock. She was given three pints of blood, taken immediately to the operating room, and a laparotomy was done. Four inches of small bowel were removed. Several perforations in the small bowel were sutured, and a laceration of the lower pole of the left kidney was repaired. The post-operative course was uneventful, and the patient made a remarkably rapid recovery.

For several weeks prior to the shooting, the patient had suffered from a dull pain in her right side. She sought relief with the use of icepacks but to no avail. She was encouraged to see a physician, but she was afraid to do so. She was afraid she had appendicitis and would have to submit to an operation. She had never been ill and had never been in a hospital except to give birth to her only child. That experience wasn't painful because it was a "natural thing."

114

THE MANY FACES OF GUILT

As the patient contemplated the operation, she thought of other things. Maybe more than a bad appendix would be found. Maybe she had cancer. Her twin sister died six years ago with carcinoma of the breast which spread to other parts of the body and left her paralyzed from "the waist down" for almost three years. She nursed her and cared for her frequently during this long illness. She had read many articles on cancer. Most likely she would never have cancer, since she had a child and her twin sister did not—and "cancer mostly strikes those women who are childless." She had read this.

One item of history of major import was slow in coming from the patient. She was not living with her husband at the time of her attempted suicide. At this time she was living with a Mr. Blank, with whom she had been living for the past four months. Four months before, the patient's husband was transferred to another city by his employer. He did not take his wife at this time because her sister was visiting her from Scotland and it did not seem wise to disrupt the home then. He later sent for his wife but he heard nothing from her. After several weeks he came back to investigate and found her living with Mr. Blank. He suspected Mr. Blank because he had been trying to court his wife for the past year, but as far as he knew never succeeded until the husband left for another city.

In assessing the motivation behind this patient's action, several important determinants must be considered. She had pain in her abdomen for several weeks. The pain did not go away with the use of ice packs. She was encouraged to see a physician, but she refused because she was afraid of an operation. After menopause she had experienced increased sexual desire. In the absence of her husband she began living with another man. This was totally out of keeping with her previous life history and her value system. It can be speculated with considerable validity that her cancer phobia grew out of an imagined physical punishment for her sexual transgressions.

With increased fears, her increased guilt cried out for punishment. On that Saturday morning fears began to mount, accompanied by a feeling of apprehension and impending disaster. The patient was firmly convinced that she already had or was threatened by a serious physical illness. This semi-delusional idea probably stemmed from an unconscious belief that such an illness represented past due punishment which was now catching up with her as well as punishment for her present sexual transgressions. This persistent pain and the suspense of a presumably impending disaster became unbearable, and blindly drove her into the misfortune she dreaded. She then yielded to the irrational and hysterical impulse "to get it over with." She fired two pistol shots into her abdomen and performed her own operation (punishment). When the abdomen was opened to repair the bullet wounds, all abdominal organs and the cavity were in perfect condition except for the bullet wounds.

The common denominator in all the symptom groups in which conscience leads to excessive and neurotic guilt is the all-pervasive need for punishment and atonement and the accompanying tendency to behave in such a way that punishment is elicited from the environment. Thus the strange paradox evolves wherein for these people success, reward, recognition, and good fortune often act as stresses precipitating increase in symptoms, whereas difficulty and hardship may actually permit them to enjoy better health and more success.

MECHANISMS OF DISSIPATING GUILT

The human psyche has many methods for dissipating or trying to dissipate guilt. These methods can be constructive, destructive, or a combination of both.

Reparation is a clear-cut, commonly used, constructive method. One makes amends for whatever damages he has done to another. A person's property is destroyed because of some act of yours, and you pay him for this act. This can be in other areas than the material. A harsh word is spoken to a friend, and this is followed later by unusually kind and polite words. A mother strikes her child in anger and then she fondles it.

Punishment is the destructive opposite of reparation. However, the two motives may work together at times in rehabilitation. To be required to pay an eye for an eye and a tooth for a tooth is punishment under the guise of reparation. Such an action does nothing to replace the lost eye or tooth. The obvious constructive step which was taken relatively early in Jewish law was to interpret the *Lex Talionis* not literally but as a demand for repayment in money of the value of the damage. Another point often forgotten is that the Mosaic *Lex Talionis*—an eye for an eye, a tooth for a tooth—was a maximum, not a mandatory punishment. This was a most humane concept which restricted the maximum punishment that could be inflicted, under any circumstances of evilness of a crime, to an amount proportional to the injury done. Much later it was perverted into authority for obligatory vengeance and retaliation.

The seeking of punishment as relief for guilt has already been discussed in considerable detail in this chapter. The psychotic may even ask for execution. Sometimes his illness is overlooked, and he goes untreated. A tragic outcome can be his killing another in order to force the State to kill him. The person who suffers from guilt feels much better after he has been punished explicitly for his conduct or after he has met with trouble. Thus the punishment can be psychic or legal.

Jonah cried out to the crew of the ship which seemed to be sinking in the storm: "Take me up, and cast me forth into the sea; so shall the sea be calm unto you; for I know that for my sake this great tempest is upon you." (Jonah 1:12).

The following words from one of the dirges in the Book of Lamentations illustrates how a person may look for punishment and even catastrophe with a measure of satisfaction and even hope (he is speaking, of course, for his community): "I am the man that hath seen affliction by the rod of his wrath . . . My flesh and my skin hath he made old; he hath broken my bones . . . He hath bent his bow, and set me as a mark for the arrow . . . He hath also broken my teeth with gravel stones, he hath covered me with ashes. And thou hast removed my soul far off from peace: I forgat prosperity . . . Remembering mine affliction and my misery, the wormwood and the gall. My soul hath them still in remembrance, and is humbled in me. This I recall to my mind, therefore have I hope." (Lamentations 3:1,4,12,16,17,19–21).

Confession is another effective and widespread method of dissipating guilt. The child confesses to his parents. The Roman Catholic Church as well as some other churches uses the Confessional. Public and communal confession has had a rich history both in religious and secular life. A United Press dispatch to the *New York Times* of February 10, 1950, told of how the contagious urge to confess swept over Wheaton College of Illinois. This spontaneous mass confession of 1500 students showed no signs of letting up even after 24 hours. The students and faculty filled the chapel to proclaim their faith and confess their sins. The demonstration began one evening when a few students went to the platform at a routine evangelical meeting to "testify" and the confessions developed into a mass movement.

Both psychiatrist and clergyman are aware that at times confession goes to a pathological extreme and becomes a symptom of disease rather than an effective method of relief from guilt.

Self-humiliation, self-abasement, self-denial, renunciation, drastic self-sacrifice, and self-punishment are all methods of dissipating guilt and each has both positive and negative aspects.

Two prominent mental mechanisms used widely in dissipating guilt are rationalization and projection. Rationalization is basically our unconscious substitution of specious, socially acceptable reasons for our deeds, which appear in a less flattering light when described objectively. We explain away many of our failures and do so relatively successfully. We reassure ourselves that we cannot be perfect in an im-

118

perfect society. The criminal in jail contends that there is no difference between him and the people on the outside. He was simply unfortunate enough to get caught. We can blame poorly administered or unnecessary government regulations on our necessity at times to use the black market or circumvent the regulations.

A first cousin of rationalization is the mechanism of projection, which is the assignment of one's own traits and motives to another. Although Macbeth was really himself the murderer, he saw a murderer in everyone else. For our misdeeds, we blame the "old Adam" in us. The story of the Garden of Eden is relived daily where Adam blames Eve, Eve blames the serpent, and the serpent blames God. Adolf Hitler blamed the Jews, and in the testament which he wrote just before his death he said that the Jews had provoked war: "It is true that neither I, nor anybody else in Germany, wanted war in 1939. It was wanted and provoked exclusively by those international politicians who either came of Jewish stock or worked for Jewish interests. After all my efforts of disarmament, posterity cannot place the responsibility for this war on me."[11]

A person who has a sense of guilt without being able to identify the cause of his guilt may seek to attach the guilt to some substitute object. The same mechanism may operate in anxiety. If anxiety can be converted to fear by finding an object to be afraid of, then one can take appropriate action against the cause of the fear. Persistent, nagging guilt feelings may also seek an object, that is, something specific and tangible to be guilty about. Then confession, repentance, and other restitutive activity can be undertaken. This type of approach to guilt resolution does not always work well and the real source of guilt may remain hidden from conscious awareness, and the object to which the guilt is attached may serve only as a concealment screen which hides what is really wrong.

Such was the situation with a 40-year-old woman whose whole life seemed to be permeated with guilt. She related her guilt to certain failings in regard to her children and her husband. There were specific aspects of her role as mother

119

and wife wherein she was not especially successful, but this was not a major failure. In reality she was a good mother and wife, and the degree of her guilt was out of all proportion to her minor failures. One readily suspected that the object of her guilt was hidden from her and her effort to handle her guilt by attaching it to certain shortcomings as mother and wife was a reparative maneuver. Deeper exploration brought to the surface the true offender.

She came for psychiatric treatment when she was encouraged to do so by her family physician and priest. She had suffered from feelings of guilt from which she never received complete relief in the confessional. She was a devout and faithful member of the Roman Catholic Church. She had a major eccentricity which annoyed and inconvenienced her family, namely, never letting any relatives babysit with her children. Her family could not understand this, and her explanations to the family and to herself were never clear or logical. In the process of treatment it was discovered that when she was about six years of age her sister and brother-in-law stayed with her some evenings as baby-sitters. When she was in bed, her brother-in-law would visit her bedroom and stroke the inside of her thighs. She had felt that he forced her to submit to this, but in treatment many lost childhood memories were recovered, and she discovered that she had encouraged him. The discussion of this incident with the clear recollection of what really happened and an acceptance of reality was a true cathartic experience for her. However, the opening up of this guilty abscess and the emotional drainage which took place were upsetting to such an extent that she remained in bed several days after the abreaction. She was then freed of this pathological guilt and felt at peace with herself for the first time in her memory. Much of her guilt stemmed from aspects of the situation which she had repressed but not well enough to give her comfort. Thus, there poured from her unconscious mind these festering guilt fears which influenced her behavior in many areas of her personal and family life.

Sympathy is a fairly common method of dealing with

guilt. Sympathy means "suffering with" and a wish to help. It involves identification with a person who is suffering from pain, defeat, loss, or misfortune. When one identifies with the suffering person, he also gains love. On a visit to Cali, Colombia, I discussed with a psychiatrist there an experience of his. He has seen for psychotherapy the wives of a number of U.S. business men who represent their companies in this foreign city. These depressed, guilt-ridden women all have similar psychodynamics.

These wives come primarily from middle class backgrounds. They feel inferior when they associate with the members of the distinguished social circle which the jobs of their husbands lead them into. Many of their husbands' associates are rich and from an aristocratic Spanish tradition. Since these wives of U.S. business men have many servants, they are not needed to clean and work around the home. With the housework taken away from this group, they began to develop symptoms. Thus, tremendous feelings of uselessness, inferiority, meaninglessness soon overwhelm them. They begin to feel guilty about everything. Prior to this, the compulsive carrying out of household duties helped them keep their symptoms in check. Their major defense is feeling superior to the person of Latin extraction, so they cannot accept help from this psychiatrist, for he is a Latin. He discovered that there is only one way for him to help them—that is, getting them involved in social work, helping the unfortunate. Such work has proven curative and restorative for most of these patients. When they give themselves in useful work to others, their feelings of guilt, inadequacy, and worthlessness disappear.

Guilt is a sign of something wrong. Often, it is a part of the structure which conceals the nature of the wrong. The goal of treatment is the acceptance of this guilt as a reality. Psychotherapists and theologians have stressed that the healing of guilt is not its erasure but its acceptance. The theologian would use the term forgiveness or the awareness of forgiveness, and such a term is not foreign today to the language of the behavioral scientist. Forgiveness, in the correct sense, is not remission of penalty, nor the erasure of the past, but the taking up of a broken relationship. This is seen in better perspective if one defines guilt as the fear of the threat of rejection by, or loss of support from, persons or powers on whom one depends for real or fancied approbation. Thus the handling of guilt calls for a reappraisal of a person's relation to the judgment of society as this is mediated and accepted by his conscience and an institution such as the church to which he professes allegiance. A self-analysis of these social factors, both internal and external, often suffices to bring the guilt-ridden person victory over irrational censorship and self-disparagement. Crippling guilt feelings should be reduced not by a rejection of all moral standards but by a discrimination between rational and arbitrary moral values and the development of an honest and friendly self-estimate and self-concern.

At this point, a passion for innocence may sabotage one's efforts to develop this honest and friendly self-estimate. To accept one's past is often difficult, and many of our efforts toward confession and repentance are, in fact, efforts to undo or disown the past. At this point, remorse tries to pass for repentance. The striving to undo or disown the past can be described theologically as "the effort to purify oneself to avoid having to accept oneself as forgiven." Our efforts to escape guilt can often become so extensive and complicated that we become sick.

A patient who illustrates this passion for innocence and effort to undo the past is a 38-year-old woman who came seeking help for the symptoms of guilt, anxiety, and depression. She was underweight and somewhat malnourished. She was well-educated and held a fairly responsible position as a secretary and administrative assistant to the manager of a small business. Although extremely devout and pious, she was plagued by bad thoughts, many of them sexual in nature. Even in the confessional booth, she often had sexual thoughts about the priest. This overwhelmed her with guilt and remorse. Once at high mass, conducted by the archbishop, she visualized the celebrant before the altar with nothing on but his hat. Her efforts to control these fantasies seemed only to cause them to multiply. She involved herself in endless rituals of piety, but these did not seem to bring relief and the feeling of purity for which she so desperately longed. One of her impressive maneuvers was her refusal to eat meat on Thursday out of fear that small bits of meat might be trapped between her teeth or in her lipstick and she would eat it on Friday, thus violating the restriction of her church at that time of not eating meat on Friday. Thus under this heavy burden of guilt, she was admitted to the psychiatric service of a general hospital exhausted and hungry for what she described as cleansing. A significant aspect of her past history was that during a brief marriage in her early twenties she had become pregnant and yielded to her husband's suggestion to have an abortion. Although forgiveness for this act was available from the Church and from God, she never found what she really wanted, for *that* was purity. Much of her effort seemed to be directed toward erasing this incident in her life. Her concept of purity was so lofty that it had to evolve out of a life of complete and continuous innocence. Thus her goal for herself was an impossible one. The scar of the abortion was always there, and she kept rubbing the scar with the magical hope that it would be erased and she would emerge in innocence.

What is the solution for one's sense of estrangement, isolation and broken relationship which is seen as a part of the picture of guilt? There is an ethical dimension beyond remorse and beyond fear of social approval. For the religiously oriented, man's essential estrangement is from his Creator. The reduction of guilt, then, must involve a new relation to his God.

At a meeting of clergymen and psychiatrists, an army chaplain told of a young soldier who came to him because of sexual impotence. He had taken a minister's daughter to a hotel room to seduce her but became impotent and could not perform. The chaplain reported: "He came to me for a dressing down and that is what he was given. A chaplain is expected to be judgmental. After dressing the soldier down, I

123

called the psychiatrist and said to him that I was sending him a patient, that I had done my job and that now he could do his."

I do not believe that this chaplain fulfilled his highest role with this soldier. This young man was deeply troubled. Possibly, he was seeking to be condemned, preached at, or given a moral beating. The good pastor, as well as the psychotherapist, has always known that the deepest guilt feelings always come from the message of grace and not from the proclamation of the law. In the world of the gospel guilt is not deadweight, but building material.

The young soldier had some awareness of the relationship of his impotence to the transgression of his moral code. Many patients, however, are blind to any such relationship. To a great extent, psychosomatic medicine is the story of how the body serves as a scapegoat for the consequences of conflict in the individual's life. The bodily symptom is the expression of the conflict. Any peace of mind by the individual in such a situation often depends upon his not seeing the connection between the physical symptom and the workings of his conscience. Therefore, in the deeper levels of his awareness he may fear the very help he seeks. The psychotherapist's willingness to accept and work with the patient in his search for wholeness is a powerful stimulus for uncovering the hidden sources of illness.

REFERENCES

1. Engel, G. L. Psychological Development in Health and Disease. Philadelphia, W. B. Saunders Co., 1962, p. 377.
2. Freud, S. An Outline of Psychoanalysis. New York, W. W. Norton & Co., Inc., 1949, p. 75.
3. Mead, M. Cooperation and Competition Among Primitive Peoples. New York, McGraw-Hill Co., 1937.
4. Mowrer, O. H. The Crisis in Religion and Psychiatry. Princeton, N.J., D. Van Nostrand Co., Inc., 1961.
5. Mowrer, O. H. The New Group Therapy. Princeton, N.J., D. Van Nostrand Co., Inc., 1964.

6. Outler, A. C. Christian faith and psychotherapy. Religion in Life, Vol. 21, No. 4, 1952, pp. 508–509.
7. Piers, G., and Singer, M. B. Shame and Guilt. Springfield, Ill., Charles C. Thomas, Publisher, 1953.
8. Rado, S. Psychoanalysis of Behavior. New York, Grune & Stratton, 1956, pp. 236–240.
9. Titchener, J. I. et al. Problem of delay in seeking surgical care. J.A.M.A., 160:1187–1193, 1956.
10. Titchener, J. I. Surgery as a Human Experience. New York, Oxford University Press, 1960.
11. Trevor-Roper, H. R. The Last Days of Hitler. New York, Macmillan, 1947, p. 177.

6

Faults or Failures in Conscience

In a disturbing fable, *Soul of Wood*, Jakov Lind tells the story of Wolbricht, a one-legged veteran of World War I, who is employed by a Jewish couple to care for their paralytic son, Anton.[10] When his parents are ordered off to a concentration camp by the Nazis, he agrees to take care of Anton in return for the lease to their apartment.

After the parents are carted off, Wolbricht does not take the easy course and turn Anton over to the authorities, for he prides himself on his honesty. At great difficulty to himself, he smuggles the boy to the country in a crate and leaves him alone in a mountain cabin with a three-weeks supply of food. Anton cannot feed himself since he is paralytic, but Wolbricht does not consider this his problem. He returns to the city to sell the apartment lease, and all the time, thinking well of himself. Suddenly he becomes aware of a bump on his forehead the size of a pigeon's egg. Wolbricht presses the bump in, but it pops out again on the back of his head. He presses it again and it pops out over his ear. He presses it another time and it reappears on the top of his head. That position is more acceptable to him, for he can wear his hat over it. So really, he feels, no harm is done.

126

FAULTS OR FAILURES IN CONSCIENCE

Lind, with merciless humor, mocks pretenses of decency in this caricature of conscience.

One does not need to live long in the world to gather vast knowledge of the faults or failures of conscience. Some of these shortcomings of conscience are minor while others represent defects of major import such as the behavior of the criminal sociopath. Although persons who seem to have no conscience at all furnish the most dramatic clinical material to discuss, they are not the primary concern of this chapter.*

THE SWISS CHEESE CONSCIENCE

A parent's acting out of forbidden, antisocial impulses through the child is a clinical concept not always easily understood or readily accepted. The following patient whom I treated illustrates transparently this concept in showing the father's role in the delinquency of his 10-year-old son.

Johnny was slightly small for his age. His upper teeth protruded and he was plain in appearance. He walked with a swagger, and his voice was loud and emphatic. He was friendly, intelligent, cooperative, and related with warmth. The therapist had no difficulty in empathizing with him.

For one year he had been involved in a variety of delinquent acts, primarily theft and truancy. Some of his activity showed considerable ingenuity. Once he left home and hitchhiked several miles to a river. There he broke into a boathouse and found the food and shelter he needed for a few days and nights. He managed to start and operate the motorboat and took frequent trips on the river. When he became tired, he returned home.

His delinquent behavior began when he joined a gang

---

* Volumes have been written about the sociopathic personality, commonly referred to as the psychopath. For example, see Cleckley's *The Mask of Sanity*.[2]

made up of four boys a year or two older than he and led by a 14-year-old girl.

Johnny's parents were former show people who traveled with a circus. After his birth, the parents decided to leave show business and locate in a city so that Johnny and his sister, two years older, could grow up in a more natural setting. The father obtained employment as a maintenance worker in an industrial plant and held this job through the years. The only connection the family maintained with show business was through guests from the entertainment world whom they often had in their home.

Therapy was planned to include every member of the family. The father was the most resistant to any kind of involvement in therapy. He would deal with the problems at hand for only a few minutes and then would discuss his experiences in the circus with which he had traveled for several years. He headed a group which had a show entitled "Crime Does Not Pay." Associated with him were John Dillinger, Sr., the girl friend of Baby Face Nelson, and a few other friends or relatives of prominent criminals. This group displayed the weapons of these criminals and recounted biographical material and anecdotes from their lives. The public was shown how these enemies of society were destroyed because they defied the law.

The father did not cooperate in his own treatment and also interfered with his son's treatment. At times Johnny was the recipient of marked hostility from his father, such as being chained by the leg in his room or not being allowed to dine with the family. The father's actions and attitude were characterized by inconsistency. Often he accused the police and others of making unjust accusations against Johnny.

When the boy's acting out behavior continued, the therapist suggested a more controlled environment, and the parents agreed to this decision. Johnny was placed in a boys' home in the community where he lived. A therapeutic plan was worked out, but again the father did not cooperate. Johnny ran away from the home numerous times, and the father was sure he was mistreated and abused there; otherwise he would not have had a need to run away.

128

FAULTS OR FAILURES IN CONSCIENCE

It was obvious that Johnny could not be handled in the community where his family lived. The only alternative was a state correctional school 250 miles away. The parents agreed to have him sent there, and the juvenile court judge insisted that this be done. No sooner were the arrangements complete than bitter complaints began to come from the father. He felt that his son was being driven toward a criminal career. He showed the therapist a picture of John Dillinger, Sr., and John Dillinger, Jr., standing side by side in an open field, and said, "This snapshot was taken just before John Jr. was sent to a reform school for something he did not even do. Shortly after he was released, his criminal career began." He discussed Dillinger's criminal record, and before leaving, showed the therapist a picture of himself and John Dillinger, Sr., flanking a large poster of Baby Face Nelson, which was captioned "Crime Does Not Pay."

The father's interest in criminal activity was a consuming one. His conscious life was a reaction formation, for a criminal lurked in his unconscious mind. He lived the life of a respectable citizen, but acted out his hidden, criminal impulses through his son.

A parent who acts this way toward a child may help develop in him a "swiss cheese conscience." The conscience functions in certain areas, but in others it acts as no barrier, control, or guide whatsoever.

In this type of parent-child relationship, a parent unconsciously encourages a child to act out behavior forbidden to himself by his own conscience. Developmentally this results in a particular defect in conscience formation in that it sanctions indulgence by the child in certain behavior or activity ordinarily forbidden.

Johnson and Szurek have shown through their research primarily at the Chicago Institute for Juvenile Research, University of Illinois, that there is no generalized weakness of the conscience, but rather a defect in conscience in circumscribed areas of behavior, and they term these "superego lacunae."[7,8] The resultant encouragement to act out often brings the person into conflict with society, and the attempt to control the impulse induces an intrapsychic conflict. For example, a child may be entirely dependable in almost every sphere of activity such as regular in school attendance and honest in his work, but he engages in petty stealing or perhaps in serious sexual acting out. Neurotic conflicts, ranging in degree from mild to severe, usually accompany such defects in conscience.

The thesis which emerges from the findings of Johnson and Szurek is that the parents may find vicarious gratification of their own poorly integrated forbidden impulses in the acting out of the child, through their unconscious permissiveness or inconsistency toward the child in these areas of behavior. The "superego lacunae" of the child correspond to similar (unconscious) defects of the parents' superego which in turn were derived from the conscious or unconscious permissiveness of their own parents.

The more important parent—usually the mother, although the father is always involved in some way—has been seen to *unconsciously* encourage the amoral or antisocial behavior of the child. The parent's neurotic needs whether of excessively dominating, dependent, or erotic behavior are vicariously gratified by the behavior of the child or in relation to the child. These neurotic needs of the parent exist because of some current inability to satisfy them in the world of adults, or because of stunting experiences in the parent's own childhood, or more likely, because of a combination of both of these factors. Because these neurotic parental needs are unintegrated, unconscious, and unacceptable to the parent herself, the child is sooner or later frustrated and thus experiences no durable satisfactions.

Often I see a mother who continuously cautions her daughter against sexual activity with boyfriends. Then she waits up until the daughter returns from a date and asks her numerous questions, about where they went, how involved they became sexually, how she felt, and so on. Thus, with one hand the mother restrains and with the other pushes the daughter into sexual involvement much further than the daughter planned to go.

A dual purpose for the parent is served when the parent's

forbidden impulse is acted out vicariously by the unfortunate child and when this acting out, in a manner distinctly foreign to the conscious wishes of the parents, provides a channel for the hostile, destructive impulses of the parent toward the child. Not infrequently, parents may blatantly reveal the child's misbehavior to schools, family friends, and neighbors, in a way very destructive of the child's reputation. This becomes a source of almost overwhelming rage in the child.

This type of acting out in children from a nonverbal countervalent signal from parent to be disobedient, for example, while asking verbally for obedience, happens usually only in the family. The order of such a nonverbal communication is probably higher than the average verbal one. In the family where the relationship is intense and intimate there exist numerous cues, signs, and other points of communication. The psychotherapeutic situation rivals the family at times in the intensity of relationship. Thus, not only do children not infrequently act out the hidden, forbidden impulses of their parents, but patients do likewise with their psychotherapists.

EMERGING IDENTITY

With the large number of broken homes in our society today, the stage is set in child-rearing for numerous problems in conscience development. A chief difficulty in the formation of conscience lies in the incapacity to effect a lasting identification and internalization of values of significant persons. One can assume that this is the result of the early loss of stable relationships with the parents, as well as the fact that the parents themselves offer most unsatisfactory figures for identification. Such situations as moving from one foster home to another, exposure to inconsistencies in discipline, and receiving serious physical maltreatment from a parent furnish the matrix for structural defects in the child's con-

131

science. Although defects to some extent may be found in many persons, it is especially marked in children who have experienced limited opportunity for satisfactory identification in early life.

Lack or loss of identity, as well as interference in identity formation may end in a variety of faults or failures in conscience, especially the kind that permit antisocial and destructive behavior.

In their efforts to predict delinquent behavior the Gluecks have pinpointed five highly decisive factors in family life: father's discipline, mother's supervision, father's affection toward his son, mother's affection, and cohesiveness of the family.[4] Usually the situation points to a father who is a harsh disciplinarian without love. The mother is busy with interests usually outside of the home and neglects the child, and then out of hostility and guilt, she overindulges the child and permits herself to be manipulated. There is no cohesiveness in the family. Firm and friendly parents who get along with each other and their children generally have the type of family environment out of which delinquents do not come.

As one's personality is molded, he responds to all the stimuli about him, whether obvious or not. The manner in which these messages or stimuli are communicated to the individual is of major significance in determining the way and the extent to which the person will respond to them. If the message is direct and clear, the individual can receive it without confusion and act accordingly. If, on the other hand, he receives a message at one level, which is contradicted at another level, the person's response is likely to emerge in an unanticipated manner.

When training is inconsistent, there are formed in the developing child inconsistent, conflicting images which cause serious confusion in his mind, as a child and later as an adult. For example, a mother filched from her husband extra spending money for her son, who knew of this. As an adult he felt he could indulge himself even illegally but felt very guilty toward his father and other honest men who worked hard. He spent his life struggling with the ambiguity of indulging himself illicitly as his mother had done and being the responsible worker and family man his father was.

An anonymous writer has developed twelve rules for rearing a delinquent or an individual with a defective conscience. Although both painful and guilt provoking to read, they are:[6]

1. Begin with infancy to give the child everything he wants. In this way he will grow up believing the world owes him a living.

2. When he picks up "bad" words or "dirty" words, laugh at him. That will make him think he is "cute." He will run off and pick up some other words that will blow the top off your head.

3. Never give him any spiritual training until he is 21 and then let him decide for himself. By the same logic, never teach him the English language. Maybe when he is old enough he may want to speak Bantu.

4. Praise him in his presence to all the neighbors; show how much smarter he is than the neighbors' children.

5. Avoid the use of the word "wrong." It may develop in the child a "guilt complex." This will prepare him to believe that when he is punished later on for stealing cars or assaulting women, society is "against him" and that he is being persecuted.

6. Pick up everything after him: his shoes, his books, his clothes. Do everything for him, so that he will be experienced in throwing burdens on others.

7. Let him read anything he wants. Have no concern whatever for what goes into his mind. Provide him with lily cups for his lips, but let his brain drink of any dirty container for words and ideas.

8. Quarrel frequently in the presence of your child. In this way he will be prepared for a broken home later on.

9. Give him all the spending money he wants; never let him earn his own.

10. Satisfy every craving of the child for food, drinks, and everything that has to do with the sense of taste and touch, gratifying every sensual desire.

11. Take his part against policemen, teachers and neighbors. They are all "prejudiced" against your child.

12. When he gets into real trouble, always defend yourself and say: "I never could do anything with him."

Middle class values dominate our way of life. Also our goals are middle class, portraying the American dream of unlimited opportunity, material success, education, and status. At the same time, society denies children from the lower socioeconomic levels the chance to achieve its goals. Middle class children are brought up to expect success and are helped by their family to achieve it, and are taught to subordinate present satisfactions to long-range opportunities. Youngsters in depressed urban and rural neighborhoods have little direct contact with successful persons, often lack an adequate family life, and are unsure about finding legitimate ways of recognition. Such children will often reflect, by aggressive actions, the bitterness and hostility they and their parents feel against the middle class world whose ambivalently perceived dominating influence is felt on every hand.

Growing out of their frustration, these youngsters are motivated to seek alternative methods of satisfaction. Since society withholds the status they seek, they look for it within smaller groups with goals they can achieve. The values of such groups are often the opposite to those of a stable society. Status may depend on prowess in gang fights, in defying authority, and in taking by force or stealth what cannot be obtained legitimately.

Thus, youngsters are not antisocial or withdrawn because they were born in an uneducated family or a slum environment and had many bad examples set for them. Their contempt for middle class values probably stems from their being deprived of higher standards, excluded from the advantages of higher values, of better learning opportunities and better living conditions. They want these benefits but feel that they are not wanted as participants in such benefits. Many of them act out rebelliously against those who are depriving them and against a society that is biased against them because they are poor or of a different ethnic group.

134

FAULTS OR FAILURES IN CONSCIENCE

It seems almost impossible for an individual to develop a sure sense of himself unless he can find aspects of his social situation with which he can clearly identify. Identifications with family, neighborhood, or city are usually adequate, but for some, identification with a larger community, such as the nation, is essential. A clear identification is difficult when a country which describes itself as a nation of democracy practices expediency, favoritism, or ruthlessness with certain groups within the nation and outside of it. A youngster may see the values of his nation, which he also has accepted without question, as cruel, hypocritical, and destructive of the individual freedoms and possibilities they proclaim. He may then respond by saying: If this is my country, I do not belong here. Such a questioning may be more disquieting than the questioning of one's own ability in living up to these values.

David Garnett mentions that, although he has come to believe that his parents and their closest friends were right in their opposition to the Boer War, he, nevertheless, suffered permanent damage, not as much from being stoned by his schoolmates for being pro-Boer, as from not being able to identify as a British boy with a British cause.[3] An aspect of the Boer War especially upsetting to him was the British concentration camps where Boer women and children were allowed to die by the hundreds in order to prevent them from cultivating the farms while their men were fighting.

In actuality, youngsters from all socioeconomic levels may have difficulty committing themselves to our middle class values. The gifted and imaginative psychologist Kenneth Keniston has done a study in depth of the processes that lead many of our brightest youth to despise and reject the society in which they have grown up and which has afforded them its best opportunities and advantages.[9]

What the uncommitted or alienated youth have in common, etiologically in Keniston's study, is the experience of having been reared in families in which the father, though often celebrated in the great society, has withdrawn from the demands of family life and particularly from those of his wife;

135

in which the wife and mother has responded by becoming seductive and treacherous in her urgent need to extract at least minimal attention and emotional support from her husband and sons. These boys responded by hating and mistrusting the father for his weakness and fearing the mother for her ability to get them on her side and use them against the father whose wretchedness brings them to despair. There is no one they seem able to trust. A pivotal passage in Keniston's argument is the following: "The alienated consciously and unconsciously see adulthood in our society as asking a price that they are unable and unwilling to pay. Unconsciously adulthood involves relinquishing for good the fantasy of infantile fusion; consciously, it involves 'selling out,' abandoning their dreams and visions, committing themselves to people, institutions, and causes which they see as making destructive claims on them. Adulthood means accepting an adult self-definition which entails limitation of awareness, openness, and genuineness; it involves materialism, boring work, being controlled by the demands of others."

Keniston attributes to the alienated young people a disaffection so deep-seated and chronic as to disable them politically: "Strong in opposition, these young men are weak in affirmation; unable to articulate or even to know what they stand for, they have little sense of self to stand on . . . But rebels without a cause can only stand against, not for; and even their opposition is diffuse and unspecific. The price they pay for this opposition, a price exacted by all societies (which must refuse sanctioned identity to their opponents), is inner confusion, disunity, and fragmentation. For this reason, if for no other, it is far easier psychologically to be revolutionary with a program than an alienated youth with only a vague set of rejections."

Apart from the influence of the complex and pathological families of alienated youth is the fact that our society has become morally insufferable. There is much in our present society repugnant enough to arouse protest; and our uncommitted youth may be the first to wither in a social climate such as ours. Yet, in spite of the young who refuse to try, most of their peers accept our way of life with its ambiguities and contradictions.

TRAVEL, LEISURE, AND COMMUNICATION

There is at times some weakening of the conscience during travel or leisure. A typical example is that of a prominent business executive who attended a convention in a distant city. In a bar he became acquainted with a girl, drank excessively, and afterward could remember practically nothing about what took place during the evening. For weeks after he returned home he was guilty and depressed. He had no energy and could not work effectively. His desk was piled high with papers of all kinds and he kept postponing any decision making. His daughter's marriage was failing at this same time and this served only to emphasize to him that his behavior at the convention might also lead to the breakdown of his marriage. During psychotherapy he was able to remember what took place that particular evening during the convention. He came to grips with this behavior and worked it out with his wife. He forgave himself and found forgiveness from those whom he loved. His happiness and productive work pattern then returned.

One who lives out his life in the town of his birth derives much support for inner social controls from proximity to family and relatives, and from their continuing expectations of him. It is known by all what kind of person he is, and he is expected to continue being that type of person. Also, if the culture of the community is relatively homogeneous, conscience is strengthened by the continuing pattern of known traditions, customs, and values. Unopposed mores are usually taken for granted and not subjected to critical scrutiny. The pattern of life from which certain inner controls were derived continues to nourish and strengthen that conscience, and life under such conditions is orderly and predictable. Few persons

137

today live out their lives in the community of their birth or in proximity to parents. We move about our country and the world with increasing freedom and speed. Immigrants have often been astonished to discover that a fellow immigrant of good reputation in the old world has, in the new world, acquired a past of remarkable grandeur.

Other changes also contribute to the withdrawal of support of conscience. Even the person who lives out his entire life in the same town finds himself in a much more heterogeneous culture than did his grandparents. In a thousand ways his town has been connected with other parts of the world and the larger society—through super highways, television, radio, movies, the products of far away factories and lands for sale in its stores, and jet airlines. The cultural horizons have receded and the diverse mores of distant cities seep in through the modern instruments of communication. When one is exposed to alien mores, he finds himself examining his native mores. As soon as mores are examined, they are often seen to be relative, and their claim to absolute validity evaporates. Thus, the conscience is deprived of that substantial support which had been provided by the unquestioning acceptance of an unopposed pattern of life.

The increase of leisure time in our culture is another contributor to the loosening of conscience controls. It is generally accepted that work strengthens conscience and leisure facilitates impulse.

THE IMAGE OF GOD THE FATHER

The place of God in the formation and function of the conscience is changing radically today. In former days behind the authority of one's father was the greater authority of God. Behind the towering image of one's earthly father loomed the vast image of God, the Father of all mankind. Both were incorporated by the child during the process of socialization. The function of God within the conscience was steadily aided by the continued existence and individual awareness of God in the outside world. This operated in the same way that the continued nearness to one's earthly father augmented the authority of the internalized father. The decline of religious belief and devotion has sharply diminished this support. The extent of the decline of belief in the supernatural propositions of religion measures the loss of one of the most important external supports to the conscience.

A remarkable series of data from the Gallup opinion poll reports that the response "religion is losing its influence" has jumped from 14 per cent of a national sample in 1957, to 31 per cent in 1962, to 45 per cent in 1965, to 57 per cent in 1967. The size of the change in the relatively short period of a decade is startling. A tip-off to what lies ahead is also suggested by the responses from the youngest group in the survey. More young adults (ages 21–29) than any other group said that religion is losing its relevance in today's world. Also, the young adults reported the sharpest drop in church attendance, a decrease of 11 percentage points. Thus, religion as an external support to conscience will influence an increasingly smaller population.

CONSCIENCE IN BONDAGE TO CLAN

Adolf Hitler told Hermann Rauschning, president of the Danzig Senate: "I liberated men from the filthy, humiliating, poisonous folly called conscience and morals." He did make murder so light a matter that the "gas buses" in which the Nazis killed many of their 6 million Jewish victims often had picturesque colored shutters like so many cottages. Also at another of the Nazi extermination centers the condemned went to their deaths to the strains of the Merry Widow Waltz.[5] One wonders about the genesis of this major dissociation and breakdown of conscience in this sick and criminal individual.

Yet, Hitler claimed great allegiance to his particular clan, the so-called Aryan group. Any action could be taken against an outside group, no matter how evil or destructive, without the slightest compunction of conscience. Within his own group of followers rules did exist governing their relationships with one another. The delinquent and the criminal usually obtain their "guilt insurance" through coverage by the group code.

The provincial nature of conscience is one of its most frightening aspects. Ardrey emphasizes that forces of enormous power, derived from the animal world, play their instinctual roles in the drama of human conduct.[1] Some of these forces are: social groupings based on the defense of a territory involved; the contest between males for superior territory or superior status; the hostility of territorial neighbors whether individual or group; and the dual code of behavior prevailing in the members of a group, demanding amity for the social partner and enmity for individuals outside the territorial bond. Although these are human instincts, they are derived from ancient animal patterns, according to Ardrey.

The behavior of delinquent gangs illustrates well the characteristics which are more primitive than civilized. For example, the musical *West Side Story*, a tale of juvenile life in the New York streets, deals with the timeless struggle over territory. There is a rigid system of dominance among males within the gang; and the individual defense of status is timeless. The amity-enmity code exists as in any animal society: mercy, devotion, and sacrifice for the social partner *versus* suspicion, antagonism, and unending hostility for the territorial neighbor.

One is not astonished at all, therefore, when scientists such as Ardrey speak compellingly of civilization as a product of evolution and an expression of nature's most ancient law— the instinct for order. Humanity's most reliable ally, then, is the instinct for order, while conscience is its least reliable ally. In fact, conscience at times plays the role of villain in not inhibiting the predatory instinct but becoming the conqueror's chief ally. Thus, the chief limitation of conscience lies in its territorial nature, for it is the mechanism whereby a society mobilizes its members against an enemy and commands individuals to make sacrifices for the common good. The human species has shown a capacity to form territorial coalitions which result in the formation of larger and larger territorial societies and thus the extension to an increasing number of individuals the expression of tolerance, compassion, and mercy. In this sense conscience has acted as a building block in the edifice of civilization.

Conscience thus has its two sides, a dark and a light one; it can organize hatred in the same way it organizes love. In the United States, a person's conscience is deeply influenced by the region in which he lives, and he may do things which offend the conscience of a person in another region of his own country. One seldom brings to his actions the authority of universal law because he is bound by a conscience that is provincial in nature and whose origins are territorial.

Ardrey separates sharply the instinct for order from conscience.[1] In both the theological and the psychological definition of conscience, I am not sure that man's devotion to order would necessarily be excluded from his inner controls. No matter where it is placed in man's psyche, one can be grateful that this shadowy, mysterious, undefinable command for order is there. Therefore, we help our neighbor replant his crops destroyed by drought, rebuild his burned home, and minister to his diseased body.

EVIL IN THE NAME OF GOODNESS

Each generation tends to perpetuate many of its strengths and weaknesses of character, often unchanged. A group of adults in our society are amoral or expedient in character. They set before their children the example of just what they are, and their children turn out to be essentially like their parents. On the other hand, a much larger group of adults are largely conforming and almost irrationally conscientious

141

in their character dynamics.[11] Usually with a high sense of moral righteousness, these people treat their children in such a way that their children turn out to be either passively compliant sheep in search of a shepherd or slaves to rigid rules and dogma. Some of the slaves to a rigid and unbending conscience choose the role of martyr or martyr-maker. The self-righteous, self-appointed guardian of morality who puts an abstract principle above real human considerations can exert a savage cruelty in the name of righteousness.

One's grandiose moralism may lead him to believe that his own ideas of social behavior are God-given and *must* be true and that anyone who has dissenting notions of morality is indubitably wrong, should be severely punished and even exterminated for being a dissenter. In following the letter of the law, one can confuse its purpose. Berdyaev in *Slavery and Freedom* and Ibsen in *The Wild Duck* indicate that one zealously and rigorously addicted to the good may end in doing injury. In the words of Cicero, *summum jus, summa injuria.*

The experience and functioning of conscience is much more than respect for and possession of moral values. There is a distinctive experience of "I should" or "I ought," implying a reference to a moral standard in the form of a general moral principle or in the form of a concrete authority. The experience involves a view of oneself and one's actions from the standpoint of some principle or authority and is, therefore, dependent on the capacity of the individual for a certain detachment from himself, for self-critical attention and examination. The obsessive-compulsive neurotic with a harsh conscience often examines a piece of behavior in quite abstract dimensions and considerations apart from its practical significance. For example, such a person may decide that to visit a prostitute is wrong because his action gives assent to and supports the institution of prostitution with all its accompanying evils and injustices; he gives essentially no thought to the actual and personal consequences of the specific act.

The individual with this type of harsh conscience is

142

guided by a firmly organized body of internalized moral rules which maintain their own autonomy. These moral rules are not particularly affected by what other people may say, nor do they permit themselves to be questioned or tested by rational inquiry. Such a tyrannical conscience is largely walled-off from the mediating influences of the individual's ego and becomes a compartmentalized fragment of the personality; it does not change and deepen in wisdom as new experiences are encountered.

Such a conscience is identified by Mark Twain in his short story "Was it Heaven? or Hell?"[13] The story tells of a pair of women who felt strongly about the evils of lying. When their doctor asks them whether they would tell a lie to shield a person from an undeserved injury or shame, their answer is "No."

"Not even a friend?"

"No"

"Not even your dearest friend?"

"No"

"Not even to save him from bitter pain and misery and grief?"

"No. Not even to save his life."

"Nor his soul?"

"Nor his soul."

"I ask you both—why?"

"Because to tell such a lie, or any lie, is a sin, and could cost us the loss of our own souls—*would,* indeed, if we died without time to repent."

The doctor's straightforward response: "Is such a soul as that worth saving? Reform! Drop this mean and sordid and selfish devotion to the saving of your shabby little souls, and hunt up something to do that's got some dignity to it! *Risk* your souls. Risk them in good causes; then if you lose them, why should you care? Reform!"

Another form of conscience capable of evil effects is the one devoted almost solely to rule conformity, with approximately full authority residing in the people around the individual with such a conscience. The cardinal principle of

143

behavior is an anxious desire to do whatever the "respected others" require. The individual finds sustaining reassurance when accepted by the "respected others" and experiences shame when found wanting. Although rules are believed in, final recourse is usually sought in the approval and support of respected authority figures. This type of person can be swayed in any direction by these respected others or can become putty in their hands. The capacity for evil in society from this type of person is great.

A set of rules which are impossible to follow, whether they come from within a person or from his environment, create grave problems for an individual. The person whose conscience consists of a collection of harsh, crude "don'ts," acts at best in a regressive manner and becomes a cowed, childish conformer and at worst so excessivly frustrated that he becomes amoral and expedient. An example of the tyranny of external rules involves the U.S. Air Force Academy honor code.[12] A couple of years ago there was an official investigation of widespread violations of the honor code. Every facet of the cadet's life was controlled by a whole volume of regulations which determined everything from the position of the clock on his desk to his uniform. For infractions he received demerits, restrictions, confinements, and so on. As one cadet emphasized: "If all the regulations were interpreted literally, it was simply not possible to live up to them." Picayune regulations proliferated, and the honor code became a remote and impersonal thing. It became less an ethic than a tool of inquisition for the authorities.

The code deteriorated into a kind of joke. A popular game was devising ingenious ways of obeying the letter of the honor code while toying with its spirit. Many forms of subtle rebellion evolved in opposition to the tyranny of rules impossible to follow. The stealing of examination questions represented adventure but also rebellions, defiant behavior against oppressors. Finally men were sent from the Air Force Office of Special Investigations and the public soon learned of the tragic scandal and the 105 cadets who resigned as a result of this.

FAULTS OR FAILURES IN CONSCIENCE

REFERENCES

1. Ardrey, R. African Genesis—A Personal Investigation into the Animal Origins and Nature of Man. New York, Atheneum, 1961.
2. Cleckley, H. The Mask of Sanity. 2nd ed. St. Louis, C. V. Mosby Co., 1950.
3. Garnett, D. The Golden Echo. New York, Harcourt, Brace, 1954, Vol. I, pp. 59–61.
4. Glueck, S., and Glueck, E. Predicting Delinquency and Crime. Cambridge, Harvard Univ. Press, 1959.
5. Heydecker, J. J., and Leeb, J. The Nuremberg Trial. A History of Nazi Germany As Revealed Through the Testimony at Nuremberg. (Trans. and ed. by R. A. Downie.) Cleveland, World Publishing Co., 1962.
6. How to rear a delinquent. (Anonymous.) Federal Probation. March, 1963.
7. Johnson, A., and Szurek, S. A. Etiology of anti-social Behavior in delinquents and psychopaths. J. A. M. A. 154:814, 1954.
8. Johnson, A. M., and Szurek, S. A. The Genesis of anti-social acting out in children and adults. Psychoanal. Quart., 21: 323, 1952.
9. Keniston, K. The Uncommitted: Alienated Youth in American Society. New York, Harcourt, Brace and World, 1967.
10. Lind, J. Soul of Wood. New York, Grove Press, 1965.
11. Peck, R. F., and Havighurst, R. J. The Psychology of Character Development. New York, John Wiley and Sons, Inc., 1960.
12. The honor code became a joke: A personal story of a cadet involved. *Life,* pp. 67–73, Feb. 12, 1965.
13. Twain, M. Was it Heaven? or Hell? In The Writings of Mark Twain. Vol. 24. New York, Harper and Brothers, n.d.

145

7

Modification of Conscience

A variety of agencies and individuals in society are involved in modification of conscience. The home, school, and church assume primary responsibility. Law enforcement agencies and correctional institutions are interested in rehabilitation and modification of human behavior but usually have at their disposal programs mostly for punishment, not through their choice but through society's failure to support such a constructive endeavor as rehabilitation. Psychotherapists, involving individuals from many disciplines and backgrounds, represent another substantial element in our society devoted to modifying human behavior, specifically the conscience.

It is difficult to separate a discussion of modification of conscience from modification of behavior in general. All behavior is motivated to solve some need or problem within the person. He uses the resources at his command to meet the need or solve the problem. The behavior observed is the result of a formula: motivating force + resources = behavior. The behavior can range from socially acceptable to markedly antisocial.

Efforts to modify behavior involve first the identification

146

of the motivating forces. These include, among others: hostility, rebellion, need for attention, need for love, need for prestige with peers, need for approval of one's own sex, need for approval of the opposite sex, and a need for security or a feeling of at-homeness in the world. If the motivating force is resulting in antisocial behavior then the meeting of the need represented by the force will bring about a change in behavior. Of course, meeting the need is not always feasible. Yet, the individual usually has many resources which can be utilized to satisfy the motivating forces in a socially acceptable way.

MODIFICATION THROUGH EXPANSION

As the child moves into adolescence, he experiences an expansion of the conscience. Contacts with teachers, older boys and girls, professional people, and merchants offer opportunities for new identifications which enrich the conscience. The necessary conflict between the older and younger generations creates a positive hunger and readiness for new ideals. This is intermingled with the adolescent's quest for independence. He discovers that an excellent way to assert his independence and liberate himself from his parents is to repudiate their value systems and treasured beliefs. The adolescent may do this, for example, by declaring himself an atheist. Also he may become involved in numerous forms of antisocial behavior. Sexual activity often becomes idealized as it sometimes does in gangs of girls or in nondelinquents in whom the same phenomenon occurs as part of an individual revolt against parents. In such situations a conscious sense of guilt may disappear in favor of the pseudo-emancipated conscience, but the old conscience often demands its pound of flesh in the form of lack of sexual pleasure, life restrictions, and secondary use of symptoms as punishment.

One cannot consider the enlarged conscience of the adolescent without considering those cultural influences which

147

impinge upon the adolescent more than the child. No definitive criteria are available by means of which the effect of cultural forces on individual development can be estimated. However, we need to consider seriously whether there are cultural forces in our country which tend to interfere with the adolescent process: the establishment of mature, genital sexuality, love for others, and a firm sense of self or personal identity. If society does not offer the adolescent adequate ideals in the form of heroic figures, his hunger for them will tend to drive him to the gang. In the gang he finds a social organization that takes care of many of the functional, instinctual, and value needs of the adolescent in conveniently institutionalized ways.

There are two central problems in the psychology of conscience. The first concerns its *development* and the second concerns its *adult structure*. The child has a *must* conscience and the adult an *ought* conscience. Fromm in *Man for Himself* calls the former an "authoritarian conscience" and the latter a "humanistic conscience."[4]

By age six the child is fairly able to obey rules even when parents are not standing over him. From that time on, acts are evaluated entirely in terms of their keeping to, or departure from, the rules laid down. As Piaget would say, the child becomes a "moral realist."[12] The habit of expecting and obeying rules is so well generalized that even at play, the child from age six to twelve is outraged if games are not played according to rules. Often the child seeks punishment after he has done something wrong, for in this way he hopes to restore his psychic and moral equilibrium. Also, he often makes little indirect acts of retribution, as well as suffering pangs of conscience.

During adolescence, the average young person decides that most parental restrictions are foolish and engages in many forbidden acts, though not without some guilt, as has been discussed in a previous section. Around age 14, special disciplinary problems develop at home and school because he will get away with antisocial acts if he can. Gradually, though, as his sense of personal identity and self-image evolves, he

148

develops an ideal for himself, the negative aspects of the *must* conscience give way to an *ought* conscience. His behavior then is not particularly influenced by fear of punishment but by a feeling of obligation. Conscience becomes a form of self-guidance. Emphasis has shifted from parental control to individual control.

However, the rigidity of the adolescent conscience should be mentioned. Since adolescence covers many years and is an extremely fluid state, both emotionally and physiologically, the identification and description of any adolescent trait by no means implies that such a characteristic is persistent and consistent throughout adolescence. According to Fenichel, after the Oedipus Complex is resolved the conscience is at first rigid and strict and that later in normal persons it becomes more amenable to the ego, more plastic and more sensible.[3] In adolescence the conscience is normally still fairly rigid. Youngsters are greatly disturbed when adults express doubts about their honesty. They are made very angry when they are warned about or accused of indiscretions of which they are not guilty. Such lack of faith in them lowers their self-esteem and weakens their assurance that they will do what is right. It suggests an alternative code of behavior which, because of their age, frightens them.

Unfortunately many adults suffer an arrest in moral development, and there is really no transformation from the *must* to the *ought*. Their conscience remains nothing more than a life-long stencil of parental and tribal rules and admonitions, and they suffer from infantile guilt and unresolved conflicts with early authority figures.

Fortunately the adolescent and young adult are usually candidates for changes and new syntheses. The developmental phase of late adolescence and early adulthood has special significance for all subsequent personal change, as has been discussed in chapter 3. This is a time of major emotional turbulence, great ideological receptivity, and maximum experiential intensity. Many present-day behavioral scientists believe that during any adult change it is necessary to revive in some fashion the predominant patterns of this late adolescent phase of life, probably even more than those of the earlier phases of childhood to which psychology and psychiatry presently direct major attention. This is not to minimize character development in early childhood but to suggest that the altering of adult identity depends upon a specific recapturing of much of the emotional tone which prevailed at the time when this adult identity was formed.

This view is suggested by William James' association of religious conversion with the "ordinary storm and stress and moulting-time of adolescence," and his conviction that "conversion is in its essence a normal adolescent phenomenon, incidental to the passage from the child's small universe to the wider intellectual and spiritual life of maturity."[7] Thus the "moulting-time" of adolescence establishes within each man a model for later adult change.

INFLUENCE OF HEROIC IMAGES

The influence of heroic images may play a part in strengthening or modifying conscience. One of the major contributions made to psychological knowledge by Sigmund Freud and Carl Jung is their emphasis on the presence and influence of heroic images within the human psyche. Freud and Jung contend that myths, folk tales, fairy stories, and classic dramas that have emerged in the course of human history are outer expressions of images within the psyche. Freud, however, focused sharply in his own psychology on the classic Greek tragedy of Oedipus Rex and made it the primary foundation of his psychological theories. On the other hand, Jung sees the story of Oedipus as but one of the heroic patterns that history offers. Each culture has its heroes, its gods, and its mythic figures exemplifying all the essential qualities of human experience.

A person's life is profoundly affected by the heroic images with which he becomes identified. One concerned with the modification of human behavior must recognize as psychic fact the push from within the personality toward identification of oneself with images that parents, culture, and collective human experience provide. Those images which have about them a heroic quality mobilize in the individual the drive toward identification with them, for in every individual, at some level of awareness, is a hunger to be a hero. When one becomes acquainted with heroic figures who loom larger than life they can challenge one's greatest potential and creativity. John F. Kennedy, for example, seemed to capture some inner image of human possibility that crossed boundaries of nation, class, creed, and race. His death, therefore, had the quality of true tragedy—the fall of a mighty prince. His life, as well as his death, mobilized in many people of all ages the symbol of the new type of man they might become—a man of intelligence, wit, toughness, compassion, and integrity.

STRENGTHENING THE WEAK CONSCIENCE

The individual with a weak conscience expresses his defect primarily in terms of society and of conformity with the prevailing cultural milieu. He is chronically antisocial, frequently in trouble with the law, profits neither from experience nor punishment, and maintains no real loyalties to any person, group, or code. He is usually callous and hedonistic, showing pronounced emotional immaturity, with lack of a sense of responsibility and lack of judgment, but great ability to rationalize his behavior so that it appears warranted, reasonable, and justified. Such a person is classified diagnostically as a *sociopathic personality*, which is clearer and more descriptive than the old term *psychopathic personality*.

Not all persons involved in delinquent, criminal and other forms of antisocial behavior have a weak or defective conscience. Some individuals act out aggressively against society to relieve a tormenting sense of guilt or because of un-

151

controllable anxiety. Other sociopathic reactions are symptomatic of severe underlying personality disorder, neurosis, or psychosis, or occur as the result of organic brain injury or disease. However, this discussion of strengthening the weak conscience is directed toward the person whose primary disturbance is that of a conscience which functions poorly in controlling instinctual impulses.

In strengthening the weak conscience, an effort should be made to manipulate the person's environment to eliminate as many temptations as possible which stimulate the sociopathic person to express his vicarious impulses.

If the person with a weak conscience can establish a relationship to a person, especially a benevolent but firm authority, the latter may be able to guide the person's actions and probably block his behavior. Hypnosis is used at times in psychotherapy to reinforce this authoritative relationship.

A teacher, pastor, or psychotherapist, by adroit suggestions, can act as a repressive moral force and as a pillar of support. The person with a weak or malfunctioning conscience may get to the point where he will turn to the pastor, psychotherapist, or teacher for guidance when temptation threatens him. Suggestions must be made in a subtle way in an effort to convince the patient that he is actually wiser and happier for resisting such activities which, as he knows from previous experience, are bound to end disastrously.

On the basis of a guidance relationship, the patient may learn the wisdom of postponing immediate gratifications for those which, in the long run, will prove more wholesome and enduring. Hopefully, the patient learns the prudence of tolerating frustration and the need to feel a sense of responsibility and consideration for the rights of others. Most of these lessons in social and impulse control taught such a person will not immediately be accepted or acted upon. Constant repetition, however, sometimes helps the patient to realize that it is to his best interests, ultimately, to observe social amenities and to exercise more self-control.

Clinical experience has shown that it is possible to some extent to modify the immature explosive reactions of the sociopath by an extensive training program, particularly in cooperative group work where the individual participates as a member toward a common objective. Adequate group identifications are generally lacking in the individual with a weak or malfunctioning conscience. The realization that personal satisfactions can accrue from group experiences may help break his defensive armor of antisocial behavior. Such an approach to correction has been utilized by certain vocational rehabilitation schools for delinquents. The goal has been, as Maxwell Jones describes it, the *therapeutic community*.[8] Part of the program is organized around building up whatever assets the individual possesses. In juvenile delinquents, vocational schools that teach the individual a trade may contribute greatly to his self-esteem and provide him with a means of diverting his energies into a rewarding and fulfilling channel.

In most cases of social deviation the one-to-one therapeutic relationship between patient and psychotherapist is not enough.[10] Group therapy and the therapeutic community can give a patient a better chance to see himself as he truly is. He will see the reactions of the members of the group, in whose understanding and acceptance he is deeply interested. Simultaneously, the group leader continues to protect him against too heavy demands by the group and its individual members. He can test the interpretations received from the group leader by the reactions of his peers and check on his own reactions to them. He can test and learn to control the consequences of his behavior in a protected environment, trying out interpretations of his own and others' behavior among equals who are in the same boat with him.

Milieu therapy, constructively structured in a very active community of children or young people, guided and counseled by well-trained and experienced adults, gives the delinquent an opportunity for an exciting learning experience. By living in an understanding, nonthreatening, moderately challenging, and cooperative environment, he learns that his concept of a hostile world, which he thought he had to fight, is wrong. He gains new perceptions that are less biased and finds new incentives and motivations to tolerate frustrations and make

153

positive choices. While taking on responsibility he practices by trial and error how to make responsible use of what he has learned for his daily living.

Schools for delinquent youth usually strive also to develop a social environment which rewards good moral behavior in all kinds of boys and girls. They also encourage the intellectualization of values and moral experiences, for in thinking about moral experiences one is led, hopefully, to the formation of moral principles.[5]

CORRECTIVE EMOTIONAL EXPERIENCE

It is possible for a profound and favorable experience to undo the cumulative effects of long maltreatment. Conscience can be rendered ineffective by the hardships of one's emotional development. The person emphasizes to himself his adverse fate in order to feel free to act destructively. This equilibrium can be disturbed by unexpected assistance or extraordinary kindness from another person. The result can be a corrective emotional experience suitable to repair the traumatic influence of previous experiences.*

There are some classic examples of a corrective emotional experience which can be drawn from literature and history. One such example is Jean Valjean's conversion in Victor Hugo's *Les Misérables*. Jean Valjean, the ex-convict newly released from a long prison sentence, underwent a dramatic change in his personality because of the overwhelming and unexpected kindness of the bishop whom he had robbed of six silver plates. While he was still dazed by being treated for the first time in his life better than he deserved, Valjean met a twelve year old boy, Petit Gervais, singing with

* An excellent discussion of corrective emotional experience is found in Alexander and French: *Psychoanalytic Therapy*.[2]

154

his hurdygurdy at his side and his marmot box on his back. When the little boy's forty-sous piece fell to the ground, the ex-convict put his foot on the coin and refused to give it back. Although Petit Gervais cried and pleaded desperately, Valjean remained unyielding. In a shocked and utterly confused state of mind he was unable to remove his big, iron-soled shoe from the coin. Only after the ragged little boy left in despair did Valjean awake from his stupor. He sprang convulsively toward the piece of money, seized it, and ran after the boy in a frantic effort to make good his evil act. His desperate searching and calling were of no avail, for he could not find Petit Gervais. ". . . his knees bent under him, as if an invisible power overwhelmed him at a blow, with the weight of his bad conscience; he fell exhausted upon a great stone, his hands clenched in his hair, and his face on his knees, and exclaimed: 'What a wretch I am!' "[6]

After Jean Valjean had left the bishop's house, he seemed to understand nothing of what was passing within him. He set himself stubbornly in opposition to the angelic deeds and the gentle words of the old man regarding his becoming an honest man and withdrawing his soul from the spirit of perversity. "He felt dimly that the pardon of this priest was the hardest assault, and the most formidable attack which he had yet sustained; that his hardness of heart would be complete, if it resisted this kindness; that if he yielded, he must renounce that hatred with which the acts of other men had for so many years filled his soul, and in which he found satisfaction; that, this time, he must conquer or be conquered, and that the struggle, a gigantic and decisive struggle, had begun between his own wickedness, and the goodness of this man. In view of all these things, he moved like a drunken man. . . . Did a voice whisper in his ear that he had just passed through the decisive hour of his destiny; that there was no longer a middle course for him; that if, thereafter, he should not be the best of men, he would be the worst; that he must now, so to speak, mount higher than the bishop, or fall lower than the galley slave; that, if he would become good, he must become an angel; that, if he would remain wicked, he must become a monster? . . . . One thing was certain, nor did he himself doubt it, that he was no longer the same man, that all was changed in him, that it was no longer in his power to prevent the bishop from having talked to him and having touched him."

Jean Valjean did not know why he had robbed Petit Gervais. In fact, Valjean's episode with the boy illuminates one of the cardinal principles in the modification of a pattern of human behavior. The question is raised why Valjean committed such a brutish act just after he had been overwhelmed by the bishop's generosity. Hugo answers the question with another question: "Was it the final effect, the final effort of the evil thoughts he had brought from the galleys, a remnant of impulse, a result of what is called in physics *acquired force*?" The bishop's act was a violent attack upon Valjean's precarious emotional equilibrium, which consisted in being cruel toward a cruel world; Valjean in response had to restablish his balance in a spiteful insistence upon being bad.

In the conversion story of Jean Valjean, Hugo describes an experience well known in psychotherapy, that whenever a symptom or neurotic attitude is attacked by the treatment, a recrudescence of the symptom usually occurs before the patient is able to give it up altogether.[2] This is the storm before the calm, the exacerbation of the morbid condition which precedes improvement.

The psychotherapeutic literature contains many clinical examples of change similar to Hugo's story. August Aichhorn's case reports on delinquents in his school present similar occurrences.[1] Sometimes tremendous effects are achieved with juvenile delinquents when the therapist's attitude is not critical and moralistic but that of a benevolent and helpful friend. The ancient biblical principle that the law condemns and destroys if it is not preceded by forgiveness is accepted as fundamental in psychotherapy. The deepest guilt feelings—those which render the person ready for change—comes from the message of grace and not from the proclamation of the law.*

At this point I cannot help thinking of St. Peregrine, the patron saint of cancer patients.[9] In the thirteenth century, the citizens of certain Italian towns were in major conflict with the Holy See. Among these was Forli, located on the Adriatic Sea, where in 1265 was born Peregrine Laziosi, the youngest member of a rich and civilly potent family. At age 18, the political and spiritual rebellion against the Church gave the acting out, antisocial Peregrine an excellent theater for action.

Philip Benizi, who subsequently achieved sainthood, was selected to go to Forli and appeal to the people through his persuasive oratory and profound sanctity. As the official Papal ambassador, he was poorly received and subjected to abuse and beatings with clubs and rocks. Peregrine struck Benizi in the face, knocking him down. The saintly ambassador responded immediately by forgiving the youth and uttering a prayer for him. Although the crowd cheered Peregrine for his violence, he personally was overcome by the meekness and tolerance of Benizi, so that in his penitence, he ran three miles to encounter him again and at this meeting confessed his guilt, cried, and begged forgiveness. Benizi encouraged

* Count Leo Tolstoy relates this unforgettable observation: "There is a yellowish grey wolf, who, winters, joins the pack, roaming the icy tundras of Siberia, sparing neither man, animal, nor child. In the heat of the summer, however, when the brush is dry and lifeless, he crawls into the peasant's back yard, licking his hands, whining for food. Such is the nature of man and the brevity of memory that the peasant feeds the bloody tooth of this rapacious beast." In this statement, Tolstoy is concerned with the nature of man and not the wolf. Man's capacity for empathy and sympathy, for giving and receiving forgiveness bears rich fruit in his interpersonal relationships. By forgiving, one brings something to life in the other person. The spirit of such an encounter has been described by James Russell Lowell: "Be noble! And the nobleness that lies in other men, sleeping but never dead, will rise in majesty to meet thine own." Thus, there are often redemptive dimensions in human relationships which mobilize the power inherent in man for overcoming failures in conscience.

him to rededicate himself, which he did. He underwent complete reformation and dedicated his life to labors among the sick, the poor, and the sinful. He joined the Order of the Servants of Mary and reestablished the Servite Monastery in his home town of Forli.

In the course of the years in his religious order, he developed an ulcerative growth on his leg which the best physicians of his time unanimously pronounced cancerous and advised amputation of the leg. Before the amputation was done, a spontaneous cure of the cancer occurred. He died in 1345 at age 80. He was beatified in 1609, and Pope Benedict XIII solemnly canonized him in 1726. He is commonly invoked for the cure, survival, and alleviation of cancer patients, for which he is best known in Austria, Hungary, Bavaria and Italy.

SOFTENING THE OVERLY STRICT CONSCIENCE

The person with the overly strict conscience is usually fearful in his interpersonal relationships of rejection, condemnation, or punishment. Such a person frequently requires psychothcrapy to attain some softening of his conscience.

A benevolent authority figure, in working with such a patient, becomes less the authority and more the friend. The tolerant and accepting attitude of the psychotherapist gives him also a peculiar attribute of protectiveness. Since the patient by himself is unable to accept his inner conflicts and impulses, he uses the psychotherapist as a refuge from danger. The belief that he has a protector enables the patient to divulge his repulsive impulses, memories, and fantasies, with an associated release of feelings. Gradually the patient discovers that there is a difference between what he feels and what is actually going on in reality and that his guilt feelings and anxiety actually have no basis in fact.

The overly strict conscience is frequently related to the

hurt the patient experienced in his relationships with early authorities. Thus, if the patient can regard the psychotherapist as a person toward whom he need not have an ambivalent attitude, he can gain an entirely new attitude toward authority. His acceptance of the psychotherapist as a real friend has an important effect on his surrendering some of his excessively strict inner controls. If he gives up some of his strict and self-defeating inner controls, he must be assured that the old punishments and retributions will not overtake him. It is in just this situation that his experience with the psychotherapist plays a vital role, because in the experience he has gained an entirely new attitude toward authority. His own conscience then is modified by his choosing a more lenient set of standards and injunctions. The conscience then becomes less tyrannical and its values modified so as to permit the expression of impulses essential to the mental health of the individual.

One of the most important ways in which the modification of the conscience can be achieved is through acceptance of the psychotherapist as a new authority whose standards subdue and eventually replace the old and intolerable ones. In the therapuetic relationship, the patient tends to identify himself with the psychotherapist and to incorporate his more tolerant values. Hopefully, the patient will achieve a rearrangement of the dynamic forces of the personality and a reduction in the strictness of the conscience.

The diminishing of the strict conscience often gives the patient the courage to face his fearsome impulses, especially anger and sexuality. In the past hc may have been hurt by expressing either aggressive or tender feelings. Sexuality may mean to him unconditional love or surrender or a desire to attack or to merge with another person. In the therapeutic relationship he learns that normal demands for understanding and affection need not be frustrated.

To understand in better perspective the operation of the overly strict conscience, one should review briefly the development of the sense of guilt in the human being. The child attains first a stage in which moral law is obligatory only in the presence of an adult authority figure. Next, he enters a stage in which any violation of the rule is condemned, regardless of the situation. The child's judgment knows no pardon. He identifies himself with the rule and condemns the violator, namely himself. Hopefully, he is able to emerge from this stage and enter another in which the action is judged in accordance with the motives of the subject. Offensive behavior of his is considered to be an act against his conscience and the interests of society. His previous rigid judgment is replaced by evaluation, which contributes to the conception of forgiveness.

The child may not progress beyond the middle stage if he is hurt in his development by rigid authority figures. Thus, he retains a character structure which gives him none of the freedom to evaluate and decide his responses in matters of morality.

The benevolent authority figure, functioning as psychotherapist, is often effective in helping the person modify his inflexible conscience. Successful change is more likely to be attained in youths and young adults, although a person of any age is capable of change. Teachers and clergymen are also capable of bringing about phenomenal change because of their professional relationship with young people open to growth and renewal. The young person is in need of face-to-face relationships with authorities who demonstrate their concern for the individual both by support and by judgment. Teachers and clergymen have this opportunity more than other professional groups.

INFLUENCING MATURE CHARACTER DEVELOPMENT

Miracles do not occur often in character reformation, for the salvaging of a maldeveloped person usually takes intensive, long, personalized treatment. Our greatest opportunity, however, is with children. Those who work with children who have immature, defective consciences know that they have to take over the security-giving functions as well as the guiding functions often performed by parents. Patience, wisdom, maturity, and a genuine caring for the child are essential characteristics for effective therapy. In the teaching of character, one cannot teach what he does not know. Improvement cannot be expected from any program unless it is characterized by genuinely understanding, ethical treatment.

The family, school and church are institutions deeply committed to fostering good character in the form of adequate inner controls. Although these institutions of society seek to develop a character structure which is rational and altruistic, they often treat children in a manner which fosters conforming, overly conscientious, and even irrational behavior.

The adult world too often exercises its superior status and authority to "mold" children or to "whip them into line." Children must be given time to debate alternatives even when it is personally inconvenient or frustrating and in spite of the fact that their choice may contradict the adult's preferences. Most adults seem to slip easily into controlling children in an autocratic manner. While a dictatorship in a family looks very efficient, the effect on the child's character is to arrest the development of rational judgment and to create such resentments as prevent the growth of genuinely altruistic impulses. "For thousands of years, the long-term effects have been ignored and sacrificed to short-term adult advantages, most of the time. Probably it is no accident that there are relatively few people who are, or even will become, psychologically and ethically mature."[11]

Some of the old methods of character development or reformation are illogical and destructive in their effects. Penal treatment seems to offend rather than help human nature. Severe punishment generates hatred; the hatred may lead to antisocial behavior or a resentful conformity to convention which has no ethical intent in it. The evidence seems clear that the punishment theory of crime prevention does not work; yet this is a difficult belief to dispel. Long ago in England

161

one could be hanged for pick-pocketing. The hangings were public in an effort to teach great lessons and therefore prevent similar crimes to that of the victim. At these hangings, pick-pocketing was prevalent among the witnesses.

The method that works in favor of mature character development is one that gives a person the incentive to behave ethically and one that guides the person intelligently, patiently, and with growing freedom to make and test his own decisions. Other methods of child rearing or character reformation often breed unthinking, rigid compliance or hostile, vengeful behavior. It is destructive to enjoin behavior solely on the weight of authority. When the issues relate to human ethics or interpersonal morality, it is always possible to explain the reasons for ethical principles in terms of entirely observable cause and effect. Convention and tradition will persist because they have functional value, but they are susceptible to blind, foolish, or immorally expedient application to be used literally and uncritically. Tradition and authority may be right on many issues, but children who are taught to obey simply because of tradition or authority are crippled in their capacity to become truly mature and intelligently self-governing in their moral behavior.

There is no heritage more subtle or important than that which we give our children by precept and example. We are not always fully aware of the influence of our success or failure in child-rearing, for what we give to our children will in turn be given to theirs.

There is an old story of an eagle that set out to cross a windy sea with his fledgling. The sea was so wide and the wind so strong that the father bird was forced to carry his young one in his claws. When he was halfway across, the wind turned to a gale and he said, "My child, look how I am struggling and risking my life in your behalf. When you are grown up, will you do as much for me, and provide for me in my old age?" "My dear father," the eaglet replied, "it is true that you are struggling mightily and risking your life in my behalf, and I shall be wrong not to repay you when you are grown old, but at this critical time I cannot bind

162

myself. This, though, I can promise: When I am grown and have children of my own, I shall do as much for them as you have done for me."

REFERENCES

1. Aichorn, A. Wayward Youth. New York, Viking, 1935.
2. Alexander, F., and French, T. M. Psychoanalytic Therapy. Principles and Application. New York, Ronald Company, 1946, pp. 66–70.
3. Fenichel, O. The Psychoanalytic Theory of Neurosis. New York, Norton, 1945.
4. Fromm, E. Man for Himself. New York, Rinehart, 1947.
5. Havighurst, R. J., and Taba, H. Adolescent Character and Personality. New York, John Wiley & Sons, 1949, p. 194.
6. Hugo, V. Les Misérables. (Trans. by Charles E. Wilbour.) New York, Modern Library, n.d., p. 94.
7. James. W. The Varieties of Religious Experience. New York, Modern Library, 1929, p. 196.
8. Jones, M. The Therapeutic Community, New York, Basic Books, 1953.
9. Pack, G. T. St. Peregrine, O.S.M.—the patron saint of cancer patients. CA, 17:183, 1967.
10. Papanek, E. Management of acting out adolescents. In Abt, L. E. and Weissman, S. L., eds. Acting Out—Theoretical and Clinical Aspects, New York, Grune & Stratton, 1965, pp. 208–232.
11. Peck, R. F., and Havighurst, R. J. The Psychology of Character Development. New York, John Wiley & Sons, 1960.
12. Piaget, J. The Construction of Reality in the Child. New York, Basic Books, 1959.

8

Confusion of Tongues
and a Stable Morality

Recently an adolescent patient mentioned how confused he was regarding a proper set of moral principles to adopt and to follow. He mentioned the new morality and situation ethics which he and his friends were interpreting as "make your own rules." He described the multiple and often contradictory voices in the field of moral teachings as a present-day Tower of Babel with its confusion of tongues. He expressed a need for some well-worked out system of values which he could examine and then accept or modify in the light of his conscience. He implied that everywhere he saw uncertainty and instability about values.

This adolescent is probably typical of today's youth. Some important ingredients are lacking for his proper development, and he is searching for substitutes to compensate for the deficiencies. For example, such deficiencies account in part for the attraction of psychedelic drugs. Recently, a 17-year-old, in writing the editor of *Time*[10] stated that society had rebelled against and turned its back on love, individuality,

164

and humanity. To get a better perspective of things he was looking forward to experiencing the psychedelic field. He emphasized that he wanted to get *inside* of things—"in the bloodstream and sightsee the system." He wanted to explore countries that most people have only sailed around.* One can only conclude that it is a sad commentary on the institutions and agencies of society which have failed to let this young man know that the most exalting experiences in life can be genuine and that drug-induced experiences only stimulate the real ones. Falling in love, a conversion or religious experience, self-mastery, the wonders of the natural world, and a host of other phenomena furnish dimensions to living richer by far than psychedelic drugs.

DEVELOPING A MORAL SENSE

Morality is generally defined as the character of being in accord with the principles or standards of right conduct, or to put it another way, the quality of that which conforms to right ideals or principles of human conduct. The word "ethics" is derived from a Greek root, *ethos,* which originally meant *dwelling or stall.* To this word the Latin translation *mos* was given. From the Latin *mos* our word morality is derived. Often "ethics" and "morality" tend to be interchanged as though they were synonymous terms; however, the word "morality" is usually reserved for behavior according to custom and the word "ethics" for behavior according to reason or reflection upon the foundations and principles of behavior.

* In sharp contrast to this young man's philosophy is that of the distinguished young composer David Amram, who speaks of the body as the vessel of the soul. If it is in shape, it tunes the mind. He stated that when he was writing his opera, *Twelfth Night,* he ran 60 laps round the Y.M.C.A. gym track every day. "It cleared my mind. By not smoking, drinking or using drugs I find I can be high all the time on life."[12]

In his novel *Dr. Zhivago* Boris Pasternack had one of his characters say regarding the repressive aspects of the Russian revolution: "The root of all evil to come was the loss of confidence in the value of one's own opinion. People imagined it was out of date to follow their own moral sense."[11] Pasternack's words call for some statement about the "moral sense" within man.

The Greek poet Hesiod, eight hundred years before Christ, wrote a poem entitled "Works and Days." It contains these words: "The son of Kronos has ordained this law for man, that fishes and beasts and winged fowl should devour one another, for right is not in them. But to mankind, he gave right, becoming the best of all things." As has already been mentioned in the opening chapter, Thomas Aquinas taught that the first principles of moral action are known to all men without deliberation, but the behavioral implementation of this knowledge requires a kind of liaison between the principle and any given action.[9] The bond between principle and act, or between law and responsibility, is the conscience. The internal arbiter is brought under the discriminating differentiation and control of the reason in the act of judging both what man knows and what man does. Aquinas speaks of a two-fold judgment: (a) universal principles which belong to *synderesis,* defined as a perfection of our reason that leads toward the recognition of the good, and of (b) particular activities which is the judgment of choice and belongs to free choice, that is, the conscience.[1] The Thomist view of conscience is the classic statement of the popular notion of the conscience as a built-in human device for spot-checking right from wrong. Paul Tillich expresses this somewhat similarly and possibly extends the concept some by speaking of conscience as the silent voice of man's own essential nature, judging his actual being. He goes on to say that even a weak or misled conscience is still a conscience, for man's essential nature cannot be lost as long as man is man. His essential nature can be distorted in the process of actualization but it cannot disappear.[14]

CONFUSION OF TONGUES AND A STABLE MORALITY

The question is often asked, "Can we teach morality?" Although the capacity for conscience is innate, and although there are dimensions of conscience that extend beyond mere socialization, much of the content and application of conscience come from the family and society. Thus the child needs to be introduced to the higher value system of the group in which he is living. Where instruction is not given or where the family and society have become uncertain of basic values and consequently have developed a collective instability and uncertainty about values, one sees a developmental defect in the spiritual and moral dimension of man. Bruno Bettelheim reminds us: ". . . . contrary to some people's opinion, youth does not create its own cause for which it is ready to fight. All it can do is embrace causes developed by mature men."[2]

The statement is often made about the difficult time every developing person must have in our society to acquire a proper sense of morality and a value system worthy of total commitment. Three major agencies contribute to the moral development: his family; his age group or peers; and the larger community with its three principal institutions of school, church, and mass media (books, newspapers, magazines, movies, radio, TV). The development of responsible behavior represents a careful blending of personal responsibility and outer controls which are furnished by agencies such as the family and school. As the child grows, there is an expected decrease in outer controls and an increase in his own responsibility as a person. Thus, in healthy growth the individual experiences a conscience transformation in that his inner controls are strengthened and consolidated and take on a guiding, monitoring, and sustaining role in conduct and human relationships.

Thus, morality provides a core integrative mechanism for the development of personality. Morality is much more than a question of prohibitions but rather is concerned with the values and definitions of appropriate behavior by which the individual governs his actions. Morality then as a part of the structure of the self concerns itself with defining

167

and directing one's life in accord with the values one has chosen. Erikson has summarized well the leavening quality of morality in society as one's ethical acts touch another: "The true ethical sense of the young adult at its best encompasses moral restraint and ideal vision, while insisting on concrete commitments to those intimate relationships and work associations by which man can hope to share a lifetime of productivity and competence. Truly ethical acts enhance a mutuality between the doer and the other—a mutuality which strengthens the doer even as it strengthens the other. Thus, the 'doer unto' and 'the other' are one deed. Developmentally this means that the doer is activated in whatever strength is appropriate to his age, stage, and condition, even as he activates in the other the strength appropriate to his age, stage, and condition."[3]

VALUES AND DEVELOPMENT

Among the many tasks which a youngster usually accomplishes as he moves toward adulthood, two relate particularly to values: the consolidation of his pattern of internal controls and the construction of an individual moral philosophy. He is faced with learning to live with heightened impulses, as well as finding a balance between desire and restraint. Then he must build a system of values which will serve as a guide to conduct and valuation appropriate to his circumstances, and which will not be just an imitation of what he has been told to believe. Although he can fail in one or the other of these tasks, healthy development depends on successful accomplishment in both, for controls and values are closely linked.

There are several areas in which youths carry out explorations, using every medium at their disposal, in their search for the type of person they want to be. Among the significant areas are religion, sex, and social idealism.

168

CONFUSION OF TONGUES AND A STABLE MORALITY

Rebellion and Rebuilding

Religion can have an important part to play in the acquisition of an appropriate value system by developing persons. The religious area appeals to youths as a medium for orienting themselves, and often reflects their attempt to establish themselves as individuals with their own identity and personal set of values.

The adolescent, as a part of his movement toward independence, feels constrained to examine and reconstruct the religious beliefs given him by his family. He may discard certain of the religious beliefs of childhood as he struggles in his search for his own set of values and his own identity. In order to become fully emancipated from his parents, it is usually necessary for the adolescent to doubt the religious attitudes, standards, and value system of his parents. Involvement with and support from his peers involve the adolescent in a comparison of his religious beliefs with those of others. Such a comparison usually results in some change, ranging from abandonment to renewed intensity.

A further word is indicated in reference to the adolescent's rebellion against the religion he has been taught. In actuality the rebellion is often against what he thought was taught him. He is rejecting chiefly his own childhood conceptions, for which he may illogically blame his culture, parents, and church. Many years may pass before he realizes that his rebellion was not so much against parents, church, or culture as against his own immaturity. Not many things can be as upsetting to parents as an adolescent, struggling with emancipation, attacking the treasured value system of his parents.

Adolescents have a need to be exposed to some structure or order of religious beliefs that they can interiorize for themselves or reject. In many adolescents there is such confusion and ignorance about religion that they are unable to deal with the specific traditions in their background. In other words,

169

permissiveness and obscurity in religion give the adolescent nothing to rebel against or to be dependent upon.

The predicament today seems to have been summarized well by Kenneth P. Landon, director of the Center for South and Southeast Asian Studies at American University: "I grew up in an era when it was still respectable to say, 'Lord, I believe. Help thou my unbelief.' Now it is more in style to say, 'Lord, I don't believe much. Help thou my use of cybernetics in determining my probabilities and options.' "[8] In such a society the adolescent's religious conflicts may not find resolution as readily as in a society with a more structured value orientation.

The institutional church appears to be needed only in a limited way by the adolescent. The group life is important when it offers opportunities and activities involving his peers. The basic ideals and standards of behavior promulgated by the church offer the adolescent a sense of structure or permanence amid the changes and inconsistencies of everyday life.

The adolescent needs some sharp directions, while being permitted the freedom to make mistakes. The church has often succeeded in encouraging the adolescent not to fear the independence of moral judgment that must attend age and experience. Fortunately, some churches are abandoning rigid codes of do's and don't's in the area of social behavior such as dating, and they are promoting educational programs of self-knowledge and the dynamics of personal, responsible love.

The adolescent seeks in the pastor of the church a person who helps him with the tension growing out of unattained ideals or unreached moral goals. The good pastor is acutely aware that each person must stumble to find his way in love, although he has a clear ideal before him. If the adolescent's conscience, however, points in a direction different from the pastor's, the pastor can search with him in dialogue but not preach to him in absolutes. The adolescent is open to direction but not to dictation.

The pastor is often rendered ineffectual as a counseling resource for adolescents if they see the pastor's job as one to condemn rather than accept and console. Often the church deals with social and behavioral problems through eradication. For example, if confronted with problem drinking the church's solution has frequently been to vote the county dry. If confronted with sexual promiscuity, then laws are passed regarding prostitution, curfews, and so on. Instead of accepting and dealing creatively with persons who participate in questionable activities, the church frequently rejects with condemnation. Such an approach has devastating implications for counseling, for if the church's major way of solving problems is through condemnation, a young person may consider the pastor as the last possible source of help when social mistakes are made.

Recently, a psychiatrist mentioned that at breakfast on a Sunday morning his adolescent son announced his atheism. Prior to that he had considered the ministry as a vocation. About the same time another physician's son, who had also considered the ministry as a vocation, announced his atheism. It was discovered later that these two newly avowed atheists were friends and had been in discussion with one another on religious matters. Both sets of parents were deeply troubled and wondered what was happening in the thinking of their sons.

It is not uncommon for an adolescent to enter a stage of atheism or probably what is better defined as agnosticism. The meaning of this fairly common experience in adolescence probably has something to do with the individual's previous relationship to both his father and God.

In the small child, the being called God is probably conceived as being human and not spiritual, for the supreme value is found in the parents. Freud attempted to show in *The Future of an Illusion*[6] that the idea of God was no more than an infantile picture of the father. Many take issue with Freud for seeming to forget that the father might also be for the child the carrier of the projection of the God image, as Carl Jung would express it. Thus, it is probably natural that the child's religious experience should be bound up with the parents. If development proceeds normally, his projections on to them are gradually withdrawn, with the result that they become to him more human and less divine.

Many a young person during adolescence is not yet mature enough in his religion to distinguish between God and father. During adolescence, one of his tasks is to separate God from father. To accomplish this, he involves himself in struggles with authority for freedom and independence. In order to clarify his confusion and begin his movement toward independence, he may reject God or father, or possibly both. After that, he may begin working through his rebellion and arrive at a new understanding of and relationship to God and father. Religion then is used in an appropriate and not conflictive manner.

Sexuality

Although focused on strongly by the adult world, genital sex is only a part of multi-faceted sexuality of youth. In the developing person sexuality serves broader purposes than genitality. This is especially true in his quest for identity and in his expression of social consciousness. These two facets of sexuality are emphasized in this discussion because of their profound relevance to the emerging value system in youth.

In Erikson's analysis of the developmental tasks of adolescence and early adulthood, the problem of individual identity is put before that of intimacy.[4] Unless the outlines of his individual being have been established and fortified, intimacy may bring psychological fragmentation. Thus, the general rule evolves, that in healthy development, identity must precede intimacy. Often the young person reverses the process and tries to affirm his identity through intimacy. The reversal has less dire consequences for the girl than for the boy. Probably this is true because the girl often achieves intimacy in some degree before she develops the kind of continuity and integrity of self which an identity resolution implies. Thus, it is not uncommon for a psychotherapist to see a girl who

172

has gained a developed identity in consequence of intimacy rather than as a precursor of it. Through intimate connections with others, the girl may come to know her own individuality and to solve the question of who she is. This reversal in girls relates partly to the nature of feminine psychic development and partly to social reality. Our culture emphasizes so strongly for the girl the need to marry that she hardly has time or energy to invest in identity-resolution until she has gained a measure of security in a stable love relationship.

Thus, the girl usually arrives at identity-resolution through the interpersonal and after she has attained a relatively satisfactory integration of intimacy and the erotic. The boy's situation is quite different in that his identity depends on his achieving autonomy and an acceptable integration of assertiveness and self-direction.

The difference between boys and girls, in identity formation, has been somewhat overstated for emphasis. To put the difference simply, a basic feminine goal is to form a lasting tie to another, and is not an individual achievement in the sense that the boy's vocational goal is. Yet for both sexes, the capacity for a mature sexual relationship is intimately linked with a sense of personal identity.

Possibly our society is cheating youth of one of his most precious heritages by letting the sexual flower, figuratively speaking, be picked when it is only a bud, thus never reaching the splendor of its full bloom. Society's intense preoccupation with genital sexuality has created both moral and identity problems for the developing person in that free sexual expression appears to be encouraged on all sides. Our sex-oriented culture may be the result of many factors, among them our worship of youth and all that is young and virile, and a denial of, or depreciation of old age and even of the wisdom born of years.

Part of our society in its efforts to control sexuality seems inadvertently to call undue attention to it. As many have pointed out, when a group insists on suppressing the sex instinct in everything the group betrays the fact that it really sees that instinct in everything. Along with the inhibitors, with their unintentional advertising, there are the exploiters of sex—those who use it to sell merchandise of every kind. Recently I saw a truck from an oyster dealer in New Orleans that had printed on its side in large letters, "Eat oysters and love longer." Thus, youth are led to believe that potency and sex appeal are at the center of our value system.

A dimension of sexuality in youth, often puzzling to adults, is the social consciousness which is linked to *eros*.[13] Nothing is more evident in the adolescent than a heightened sense of the erotic. Simultaneously one usually sees a widening and deepening of the ocean of goodwill. The different types of love sustain, feed, and strengthen one another in the adolescent, for he does not separate *eros* from *agapé*. The feeling of love that permeates his life, that helps him relate to the opposite sex, is closely akin to the feeling that is his love for God or a Higher Being. When he carries a sign saying, "make love, not war," his activity may appear depraved to many adults. But is it? The adolescent's involvement in social reforms, sit-ins, and picket lines is not a renunciation of genital sexuality or a sublimation of the libido but an expression of the same driving force in his life.

In an adolescent's love for his girl, God becomes close, maybe for the first time, through the prism of the relationship. The beloved one is often the only person who can make God seem real. Maybe the adolescent is reemphasizing for us an ancient truth that one must know love if he is to know God.

The adult, in contrast to the adolescent, usually distinguishes sharply between *eros* and *agapé* and draws a clear line between genital sexuality and social consciousness. Probably it is adult psychopathology that has created a great deal of sexual conflict in the growing person. It is refreshing to see youth wed *eros* with *agapé*.

The potential for idealism in regard to sexual life, and the dignity that it should have, has been limited to the sexual without bringing in the much wider dimension of personal love, the totality with which love engages the whole of one's personality. Because there has been such a fragmentation

174

or a differentiation made in the various approaches to love, the one has suffered at the expense of the other. The problem of integrating the sexual with human and divine love is the urgent problem of our day.

Social Idealism

In the inner struggles which erupt at puberty, social concerns appear to be an important part of the young person's life. The reasons for human existence are heatedly debated. The desire to do something to improve the world is conspicuously present and often expresses itself in a concern for world peace. The religious man who fights for social justice may become his ideal. As one would suspect, the psychological origins of the adolescent's religio-social idealism lie in part in his yearning for peace within himself. Through the mental mechanism of projecting his inner turmoil onto the outer world, his yearning for peace within himself may take the form of a wish for world peace and social accord. Upheaval in the outer world intensifies the inner conflict of the adolescent, for he needs the steadying influence of moral strength and unity in the world around him. A stable environment helps immensely in meeting the emotional needs of the conflict-ridden youngster. Also, religious observances with festive ceremonics and meaningful symbols introduce a stable rhythm into the adolescent's family and community life.

Recently in a study I carried out with a hundred college students[7], a number of them spoke of conflicts related to social issues. Hypocrisy of religious parents and other socially responsible people in regard to social issues caused pain and confusion. What was most disturbing was the effort of the "faithful" to bend the biblical teachings to fit their hates, prejudices, or bigotry. The adolescents stated that they would have been less shaken in their struggles if the adult world had acknowledged religious precepts as ideal, and at the same time acknowledged their inability to attain the ideal in their actions. But twisting or distorting the structure of religious morality and idealism, the adolescents felt, left them with no fixed point on which to orient their values or conduct. At the same time, they, themselves, often found that it was easy for them to profess one thing and act in another way. In such circumstances, when their consciences ached, they found a little comfort in meditating on the hypocrisies of religious people, including their parents.

"Am I my brother's keeper?" should not be casually asked youth, for he may take the question seriously. If the community has concern for *your brother,* it also has concern for *you.* In the Old Testament story of Cain and Abel, God spoke to Cain and said, "Where is Abel thy brother?" A question could have been addressed also to the slain Abel: "Where is Cain thy brother?" Both questions are relevant to adolescent psychology. The victor and the victim must both examine their behavior in human relationships. A basic part of human morality is respect for the other person and a readiness for constructive cooperation in an atmosphere of mutual respect.

In the young person's search for inner harmony nothing is more helpful than an adult example of mutual understanding, cooperative living, and devotion to the principles of equality of all human beings. Respect for personality, regard for the rights and feelings of others, and commitment to the common good represent moral and spiritual values. Effective spiritual-moral commitment is the only safe and hopeful way of giving youth the structure of social peace needed for him to find inner peace.

CREATIVE TENSIONS REGARDING MORALITY

The impression today is that pleasure comes only from the erotic, immoral, and unlawful, and the pursuit of it is "smart" and "in." Not much support is given to the thesis that pleasure can come from self-mastery and self-discipline.

176

CONFUSION OF TONGUES AND A STABLE MORALITY

Yet stories such as that presented in the *Bridge Over the River Kwai* strike a responsive chord in youths, because they see a higher value in the disciplined life than they have ever known.

Unfortunately, new developments in both religion and psychiatry have been branded as promoting permissiveness in morality. Many young people interpret the new morality as affirming no established standards but declaring that *all* decisions are relative. The death of God theology, probably through a misinterpretation of its meaning, may be removing a source of both judgment and strength. Because of its non-judgmental attitude, psychiatry is often accused of moral indifference.

Where then will young people turn for certitude amid doubt, for light hidden in shadows? Whether they declare themselves indifferent agnostics or militant atheists they will continue to have psychological needs for direction, for a message of redemptive hope, and a kind of sanction that some things are eternal. And regardless of the freedom they may demand most of them feel more comfortable if limits are set, if some guidelines are evident, and if the adult world cares enough about them to help them avoid disaster.

Some day they may discover that the new morality seeks only to free them from a torturous and impossible obedience to rigid, external standards in order that true morality can emerge through their own nature as they are made increasingly aware of their own depths and of the extension of these depths beyond themselves. In situation ethics or the new morality, law is reduced from a statutory system of rules to the love canon alone. Precepts are replaced with the living principle of *agapé* in the sense of goodwill at work in partnership with reason.[5]

Also, hopefully youth will learn that psychiatry is not morally indifferent nor does it advocate uninhibited self-indulgence. It is rethinking its position on the causes of crime, delinquency, and other forms of antisocial behavior and is questioning the assumption of relating antisocial behavior to emotional illness or extremes of poverty, rather than to the

177

absence of, or to faulty, value education. Psychiatry is fully aware that if religious, social, and moral values are not presented to children in their formative years, then they most likely will lack them. Also, psychiatry is aware that in its efforts to understand and explain antisocial actions it has not worked equally as hard in urging that such actions be controlled and restricted.

In the young person's search for acceptable values and controls, probably at no stage in his life should he be free from creative tension regarding morality. The individual must continually balance and weigh his actions in terms of how generally recognized absolute values can be put into action in the context of his group's values and his own personal values. He will find that his struggle will lead him beyond the new morality.

Although situation ethics may free the individual from traditional moralism, it fails to come to grips with the need for man to rely on more than personal integrity in the social context as he sees it. Although love is stressed as the guiding principle in all behavior, situation ethics fails to recognize that man, left to his own devices, often deludes and defeats himself even when his intentions are noble. Morality can never be completely an individual matter because of its interdependence with group morality.

Thus, the individual's moral commitments are influenced by his social matrix and the judgments and evaluations of his peers. His behavior is integrated by the moral commitments to himself and to his society according to a whole range of social values.

In his search for his value system, the adolescent, mentioned earlier, finds around him only a Tower of Babel with its confusion of tongues. In spite of this serious indictment of our society, many of this adolescent's peers are able to tune out discordant voices and are identifying the constructive forces they need to acquire and consolidate a mature morality. Such an accomplishment in our present type of world says something special about the essential nature of man.

CONFUSION OF TONGUES AND A STABLE MORALITY

REFERENCES

1. Aquinas, T. De Veritate. Q. 16, Art. 1; Q. 17, Art. 1.
2. Bettelheim, B. The Problem of Generations. Daedalus, 91(1): 115, 1962.
3. Erikson, E. H. The Golden Rule and the Cycle of Life. Harvard Medical Alumni Bulletin, Winter, 1963.
4. Erikson, E. H. The Problem of Ego Identity. J. Amer. Psychoanal. Ass. 4:56, 1956.
5. Fletcher, J. Situation Ethics. The New Morality. Philadelphia, Westminster Press, 1966.
6. Freud, S. The Future of an Illusion. (Trans. by Strachey, J.) Standard Edition, Vol. 21, London, Hogarth Press, 1961.
7. Knight, J. A. Religious-Psychological Conflicts of the Adolescent. In Usdin, G. L., ed. Adolescence, Care and Counseling, Philadelphia, J. B. Lippincott Co., 1967, pp. 31–50.
8. Landon, K. P. The Eternal Verities. Family Forum. Oct. 1966, p. 1.
9. Lehmann, P. E. Ethics in a Christian Context. New York, Harper & Row, 1963.
10. "Letters" section. Time, July 21, 1967, p. 10.
11. Pasternack, B. Doctor Zhivago. New York, Pantheon Books, Inc., 1958.
12. "Rising American Composer" (Close-up/David Amran), Life, August 11, 1967, pp. 33–36.
13. Seeley, J. R. The Americanization of the Unconscious. New York, International Science Press, 1967, pp. 436–446.
14. Tillich, P. Morality and Beyond. New York, Harper & Row, 1963.

Author Index

AUTHOR INDEX

Subject Index

SUBJECT INDEX

187

SUBJECT INDEX